JFK FYI

Gary B. Haley

40+ YEARS OF READING AND RESEARCH. ENJOY!, THEN RETURN TO ANY LITTLE FREE LIBRARY.

Gary

20241015 1442

JFK FYI

ISBN: **9781957218229**

www.jfk.fyi

Publisher:
Have Coffee Will Publish
(www.HaveCoffeeWillPublish.com)

Editors:
Ines "The Wicked" Kirkpatrick
English professor, library director and world class editor.

Rhonda Lee Carver
Editor extraordinaire and award-winning author.

Contributing Editor:
Have Coffee Will Edit
(www.HaveCoffeeWillEdit.com)

A big thanks to **brilliant** proofreaders:
Jane Garland Whitmeyer, Megan McCauley and Joyce Walker

Second Paperback Edition

Preface

JFK FYI is a fact-based historical narrative novel that reads more like an adventure story than a history book. Still, a great deal of effort and research went into making sure everything is historically accurate so that readers can enjoy the highlights of a half-century of seemingly unrelated events and reactions. Some of those scenarios ultimately converge within a few short moments and change the course of humanity.

This novel is not an attempt to solve one of the most tragic and intricate mysteries in modern history. Nor do I have any desire to add more nonsense to all the Kennedy assassination conspiracy theories, which have been completely out of control since an hour or two after the shooting took place. I merely wish to share—summarize, really—what I have learned from many years of researching and reading about the reasons why *any*one would want to assassinate one of America's most popular presidents.

About forty years of research and reading led to the creation of *JFK FYI*. I estimate that I read and studied some two million words while writing this novel. While putting all the facts together, I eliminated all data sources written after the assassination, i.e., after the misinformation/disinformation became prevalent. I based this novel, except for the summary at the end, on the facts that were documented before the assassination.

For more notes and information, or to contact me, visit www.jfk.fyi

I hope you find this slice of history as enlightening as I do.

Thanks to...

The dedications found in many books have become one of my favorite things to read when enjoying someone else's work. I find that it often provides a glimpse into the author's mind and initiates the trust relationship that helps people connect and engage with the storyline. Now that I find myself privileged enough to owe a few debts of gratitude of my own, I feel that *writing* "Thanks to..." dedications is far more satisfying than reading them. I hope you enjoy this as much as I do.

Thank you to all the people who helped me complete this novel. You know who you are. I cannot possibly list everyone who contributed in one way or another, but I would like to make an offer of genuine gratitude to a few people who played the biggest roles in helping me write *JFK FYI*.

I'd like to thank my two daughters and, more recently, my son, who were and are very tolerant of me spending too much time researching and writing. I was a single father for my girls back in the '80s and '90s, and no doubt should have spent the time with them instead of writing, but, hindsight, right? My son is still young, but my daughters have long since grown and gone and have kids of their own, who are also perfect, so it looks like my daughters won't get the opportunity to use all that experience they acquired practicing tolerance. *Thank you, kids. Thank you for your tolerance and understanding. I love you.*

My wife and I have been married for years now, and she is still my best friend. She also happens to be one of the most brilliant people I've ever known. She deserves far better than the likes of me, of course, but hopefully she won't realize that for decades. She, too, has patiently tolerated too much time alone while allowing me to focus on and finish this project. She has also acted as a capable editor from time to time and always has a fresh perspective that accompanies the occasional reality check. *Thank you, my Love!* :*

Speaking of reality checks, my friend Janet Barfoot provided just that as well, in the form of invaluable feedback at key moments in the evolution of this manuscript. Few have read as much about this same subject as Janet, so I appreciate her insight, experience, and wisdom, even though she has never seen a single episode of *Star Trek*. Seriously. None of the TV series. None of the movies. Can you imagine? Shocking! *But, thanks, Janet.*

I wish I could somehow thank my ancient ancestors who passed on to me the drive it took to consistently work eighty to ninety hours per week. This is what has allowed me to work on projects such as this, others like it, and a couple of jobs, all at the same time. I suppose the best way to thank them is to pass on their genes to others, or maybe the best way to show my appreciation is to teach those close to me to relax. Not sure on this one.

And of course… Thanks, Mom. Just in case I've never said it before, or if I have not said it enough, thank you for giving me life. It has certainly been a good one!

Other Books by Gary B. Haley

The Attunist Trilogy:

What if you realized that you had the ability to truly make a difference? What if you developed the means to manipulate or kill some of the worst people society has to offer? And what if you knew that it would be impossible for anyone to prove you were responsible? How far would you go?

The Attunist Trilogy is about a man who becomes attuned to the fact that he has such abilities. As he embarks upon a crusade that closely resembles crime-fighting, drug dealers and weapons traffickers soon start turning up dead all over New York City. He seizes large sums of money from hardened criminals and uses it to take out gangs and illegal drug networks. Some of the risky and dangerous situations he gets himself into, however, do not leave him unscathed.

The Attunement
www.TheAttunement.com

The Attuned
www.TheAttuned.com

The Attunist
www.TheAttunist.com

JFK FYI

1918, New Orleans

An eight-year-old boy with calloused hands and blistered feet stood at a candy counter. Out of the corner of his eye, he looked to see if anyone was watching. Alone, he loaded his pockets. Hard rock candy went into one, and boiled, salted peanuts in the other.

To justify his presence in the store, he continued to shop for an item within his means. After a moment of feigned indecision, he settled on a bottle of Coca-Cola.

He was too young to fully understand the subtleties of thievery, yet he already knew more than many seasoned criminals. The lesson plan of that moment was to avoid the attention that would prevent him from returning to that store.

As he approached the counter, drops of condensation fell from the ice-cold Coke bottle onto the wooden floor, turning patches of dust into tiny, splattered mud puddles. The old wooden floor creaked under his footfall as he realized that the only nickel to his name was at the bottom of the pocket filled with hard candy.

He stifled his panic, even though he was almost overcome with fear, but remained cool and collected. He struggled to find the nickel in the depths of the frayed pocket, which was sewn so roughly and unevenly that the nickel had become clutched in a nook in the fabric.

Walking up slowly, he took his place in line behind the only other patron in the store, a large-framed woman in her fifties buying bandages and other first-aid supplies. Long before he had found the elusive coin, the woman hurried away, taking with her his cover and an obvious story of her own.

Unconcerned about the woman and her woes, the boy, now in full view of the man behind the counter, continued to dig through the candy. A few pieces had become sticky from sweat on his palm.

The search for the nickel became a heart-pounding pivotal point in his shoplifting career. For the first time in this new way of life, he debated whether he was cut out for this edgy lifestyle. But he somehow found the "courage" to force his fearful feet to move forward and fill the void left by the woman.

Uncertain, and reconsidering his initial plan of simply bolting from the store, the boy set the Coke on the counter, doing his best to appear as nonchalant as a shoplifting kid could appear. He heard the muffled rattling of the candy as he groped through the depths of his pocket and wondered if the man behind the counter could also hear it. His young mind raced.

Might as well be a rattlesnake in there drawing attention to itself.

He suppressed his growing fears, knowing that if he could hear the telltale sound of the shoplifted goods, the big, burly man behind the counter could surely hear it as well. Time slowed. His heart rate scrambled.

My face is as hot as it gets when I'm out working in fields of crops.

Looking at him with something approaching impatience laced with aggravation, the man tilted his head, pursed his lips slightly, and raised his eyebrows in a silent, "Well?"

Finally, he found the nickel and labored to separate the sticky candy from his sweating palm. He slapped the shiny new 1918 Indian Head down on the counter, buffalo side up. He smiled his most convincing smile.

With one big finger, the storekeeper attempted to slide the nickel off the counter into his other hand, but the sticky coin hung from his finger. He wiped the nickel and his finger briskly against his overalls and dropped it into the cash register.

The boy grabbed his Coke and headed for the door. Before he could step through to freedom, he heard the man boom with the remnants of an Italian accent, "That was-uh your first, your last, and your ONLY chance, boy. Do not forget about this-uh break you're getting from me today! No?"

The man's narrowed gaze was an obvious threat. Fear welled up within the young thief again. Yet as he stepped out of the store into the bright sunshine, the budding young con man experienced exhilaration. He made his way through the dusty streets of Little Italy as fast as his blistered feet allowed him. Despite getting caught, he knew he had gotten away with stealing a couple of handfuls of goodies and elatedly thought, *"I know I can do it again!"*

Meanwhile, the son-in-law of the store owner parted with his own fifteen cents, his estimation of the worth of what he thought the boy had stolen, and paid for the merchandise.

He slammed the coins in the proper sections of the cash register tray, mumbling, "A child that young ought not to have calluses on his hands and blisters on his feet."

The moment the kid had walked into the store, he had recognized the slight, blister-induced limp from his own childhood experiences as an immigrant farmer's son, laboring every day on the plantations along the banks of the Mighty Mississippi. He stood behind the register for a long while, lost in the harsh memories of his youth.

Outside, the little hoodlum moved briskly up St. Louis St. without a care in the world. He tossed peanuts into the air and caught many of them in his mouth. Still just a child, he thought, *"it's funny how the name of the street has 'St' at both the beginning and the end of the street sign."*

As he crossed Bourbon Street on his way back to his family's home in Metairie, he pelted a dog with a peanut.

Just over a year later, the boy walked back into the old country store, only this time he wasn't limping, and he wasn't there to return the kindness that the man behind the counter had shown him. Recently turned ten, the boy already had the sharpened and honed skills of a professional shoplifter.

Smoothly palming a small knife with one hand while using jerking, swiveling motions as a practiced distraction tactic with the other, he pretended to shop for hand tools. He reached out with one hand to replace one tool and pick up another while stealthily using his other hand to slip the small knife into his back pocket.

The big, burly man still worked in the store and recognized the boy as soon as he came through the door. The shopkeeper pretended to be busy dusting and straightening things behind the counter, but he was watching the boy through various distorted reflections in tins and glass containers. He had been in the merchant business long enough to recognize the distraction tactics the boy was using, and shook his head in sorrow and disgust as he watched the shoplifter slide the knife into his back pocket.

As the boy continued shopping, the shopkeeper moved stealthily out from behind the counter and sneaked up behind the known thief in the next aisle, avoiding all the particularly creaky boards in the floor. Quickly standing up, he reached over the shelving and grabbed the boy roughly by the back of the collar. The boy dropped the contents of his hands, raised both arms, and slipped completely out of his shirt. Before the man could peer over the row of shelves to figure out what had happened, the boy was almost to the door.

Thirteen months later, the little thief, determined to steal something from this man without being caught, incorporated the help of other younger Italian-heritage kids from the very area he was targeting. The boy was not only successful with this new plan, but also still found his victories rewarding, not caring a bit that each victory was someone else's loss.

One of his favorite plans, copied from a rival gang, involved three of his adolescent followers entering a store, where two of them immediately staged a fight. During the distraction, the boy snatched things up on his way out, yelling for a nonexistent mother or father who would not answer or come running. The boy would then run all the way to a predetermined location, usually somewhere along muddy, slow-rolling waters, to meet the leader of their gang, where they both waited until the other two showed up.

On this day, a nine-year-old with bushy eyebrows ran up under a huge magnolia tree, shouting, "Calogero! *Calogero*! Lookee what I got!"

Calogero Minacore jumped off a lower branch of the tree, snatched the box of Oh, Henry! candy bars from the younger child's hand, and punched him in the eye. "I told you to call me Carlos. Carlos Marcello."

Trying not to pucker up and cry, the younger boy accepted this behavior as normal and apologized. "I'm sorry, *Carlos*. I forgot."

Recognizing the boy's submissiveness, "Carlos" smacked him in the face again. Though the boy clenched his teeth, his loyalty was sealed forever.

"I don't like the way you said that. When you address me by my street name, make your respect convincing."

"Okay, okay, Carlos! I got it!"

The little hoodlums' efforts evolved significantly over the next few years, and before long, despite Carlos Marcello being barely a teenager himself, he was leading several gangs of teens who took turns knocking over stores and other enterprises all over the New Orleans area.

During this era in American history, such crime and violence was prevalent in most big cities and in the small towns that surrounded them. Another type of criminal flourished as well, but used a completely different set of organized crime tactics that proved far more effective at channeling other people's money into their own pockets. These people appeared to be legitimate businessmen.

1924, September 26, Cleveland

Late in the chilly autumn Cleveland evening, the soothing sounds of waves breaking on a rocky shore permeated the night air. Low, gray clouds hid the twinkle of the stars, but were not quite thick enough to obscure the sliver of glow from the moon almost directly overhead.

A fine, misty spray floated in the northwesterly wind, carrying with it the fresh aroma of the open waters of Lake Erie. Occasionally, a hint of a slightly fishy odor mingled with the refreshing breeze. The odor just missed being unpleasant but was strong enough to be noticed from time to time.

Such was American politics in the early 1900s. Something fishy was going on far too often.

High above the industrialized beach, in a corner of a large wooden warehouse, the bare window of a darkened, unheated office overlooked an old pier. In that window stood a tall, well-educated man wearing a bowtie and crimson sweater. He used binoculars to see out over the lake. The poorly insulated window allowed small surges of brisk air to seep in and interact with the man's breath.

A foggy patch of condensation appeared on the dusty glass. When the moisture began to obscure his view, the man pulled a silk handkerchief out of his back pocket and patiently dried the damp spot. He raised the powerful binoculars to his eyes again.

Behind him, a disorganized office was crowded with several file cabinets that surrounded a wooden desk cluttered with layers of unfinished work. Some hapless clerk might never have the time to tend to the tumbling paperwork.

One small area of the desk was kept tidy, and in the center of this clean spot stood a framed black-and-white photograph of a happy family wearing what might be Easter finery standing in front of a modest, turn-of-the-twentieth-century home.

The man in the photograph had a hardened look to him, as though his entire life had been spent trying to surmount a never-ending chain of difficult tasks, all of which had aged him too quickly. He appeared to be much older than the vibrant woman tucked against him, even though they had been high school sweethearts who'd graduated the same year.

But the man in the picture was *not* the same man who stood at the window monitoring the activities aboard two boats a few hundred yards offshore. The man with the binoculars had no idea who the people in the photograph were, and didn't care as long as the business was turning a profit.

The flag on the larger vessel fluttered in the stiff breeze, but the man in the window could clearly see the Canadian maple leaf it boasted. Two crew members on her lower deck handed down a crate to the crew in a smaller, single-deck boat. While the heavy wooden box changed hands, two-foot waves were squeezed between the boats. The compressed swells sprayed a cold mist that covered their gloves, arms, and faces.

One of the men in the smaller boat kneeled and opened the crate with a crowbar. Another leaned over to inspect the contents. Nodding, the inspector handed a bulky envelope to a man who had stepped out of the darkness on the larger boat. He was smug and dressed far too neatly to be a crew member. The Canadian businessman pulled a stack of money from the envelope and, with exaggerated deliberation, counted every bill under the dim light of a swinging lantern. Patiently, he turned the bills as he counted so that they all faced the same direction.

Satisfied, the man nodded to the crew, who quickly passed a couple of dozen crates down to the smaller boat. Crew members threw a worn tarpaulin over the cargo, tucking the edges in under the crates with care, as though they were putting a child to bed.

The larger boat roared off into the night, splashing through the waves, bellowing foul black smoke from the prop wash. The smaller boat gently rocked, leisurely making its way back to the pier below the office window where the man in the bow tie still watched.

Despite the lack of light and the persistent mist that hung in the air, the men docked and transferred the crates into a 1923 Model T pickup. Two of the men climbed inside and drove away.

Joseph "Joe" Kennedy Sr. stepped over to the southwest window and wiped away another circular clearing in the dust. He pressed the binoculars back to his eyes in time to witness a squad car stop the truck before it had travelled a quarter of a mile from the pier.

Without reaction, Kennedy watched the tough-guy Cleveland cops poke their nightsticks through the contents of the bed of the pickup. One of them approached the driver and made threatening gestures with his nightstick until he was handed an envelope. As they returned to their patrol car, one of the cops removed an object from a crate and took it with him.

After the truck and the police car were gone, Kennedy lowered the bulky binoculars and allowed his arms to rest for a few moments. He stared out until the distorted taillights faded away.

This is still cheaper and easier than secretly manufacturing liquor, and my profit stays the same.

The truck went about its business, its passengers aware that the police still followed them. A safe assumption would be that the police were ensuring the deliveries safely reached their destination.

The gangsters drove straight to what appeared to be a family residence in an affluent Cleveland suburb. Inside such a nice home, one might expect to find respectable, law-abiding citizens dining at a well-appointed table, but instead, the sickening, cloying stench of marijuana and opium would be overwhelming to anyone unaccustomed to attending a speakeasy.

High rollers, already high, rejoiced at the new delivery to their party, happily trading their opium pipes and roach clips for shot glasses, and willingly handing over disproportionate amounts of cash for commercial brands of Canadian liquor.

Outside, the Model T pickup rushed away to deliver more contraband to several more speakeasies in and around Cleveland, patrol car in tow.

1924, September 27, Cleveland

During brunch at one of the finest restaurants in town, a piano player played his classy rendition of a show tune currently popular on Broadway. At an elegant table with a perfectly white, luxurious tablecloth, on a semi-private balcony overlooking Lake Erie, a dirty envelope changed hands.

This envelope could be termed a package, though, for it was bulging with twenty- and fifty-dollar bills. A future ambassador to the Court of St. James in Great Britain and father of future senators and a president of the United States, showed no sign of shame at collecting a tidy profit from his contact with "The Mob." Leaving his breakfast unfinished, Joe Kennedy tossed his napkin onto his plate and jumped into a borrowed touring car. On this trip back to Boston, he was accompanied by a business associate and two well-known blonde bombshell Broadway performers.

He had always known that petty crimes were simply not worth the effort, though he discovered long ago that one could make huge profits through *organized* crime.

During the next few years of Prohibition, Joe Kennedy Sr. would make many thousands of dollars. This is the equivalent of *hundreds* of thousands of dollars in the 2020s. All from quenching the illegal thirsts of alcoholics in several American cities.

1938, January 5, Boston

Years of hardship during the Great Depression had taken a heavy toll on everyone but the wealthiest. Many people lost fortunes and became destitute while most everyone else lost their life savings. For those people, the future looked so bleak that there was a steep increase in suicide.

With jobs scarce and money tight, most people wore worried expressions on their faces as though it were their favorite old wrinkled shirt. A surprisingly harsh winter had produced the most snow in the past few decades, compounding the difficulties for New Englanders.

Despite Franklin D. Roosevelt nominating Joe Kennedy Sr. Ambassador to Britain, the Kennedys hired additional workers they didn't require to help maintain their estates. No one forced them to spread their wealth. They helped fellow Bostonians because they knew the Great Depression would not last forever.

1943, August 1–8, Solomon Islands

For close to four years, extraordinarily narcissistic people had been forcing most other humans to feel the anguish of World War II. Arrogance and egos were already responsible for taking the lives of hundreds of thousands of people, probably as many animals, and destroying large sections of the surface of our planet.

Despite having the option of not serving in the military because of a bad back, John F. Kennedy volunteered, but to accomplish this, he had to enlist the help of the Director of Office of Naval Intelligence, Captain Alan Kirk, to bypass the Navy's physical. After almost two years in the Navy, Lieutenant John F. Kennedy was given the command of the wooden Patrol Torpedo boat, PT-109.

Kennedy was ordered to join other PT boats in the Solomon Islands, on the western side of the South Pacific, where over 900 islands dotted the region. Through these islands, the Japanese Navy regularly ran supply ships, which the U.S. Navy had dubbed the "Tokyo Express." The fleet of PT boats was tasked with disrupting those resupply efforts and sinking or turning back as many Japanese ships as possible.

On the night of August 1, 1943, Lt. Kennedy and twelve crew members joined fourteen other PT boats in an effort to intercept four Japanese destroyers, three of which were transporting fresh troops and supplies to Kolombangara Island.

Stars were the only source of light that night. No moon lit the sky, nor did lights twinkle aboard the boats. The only way to spot one of the larger Japanese destroyers was to catch glimpses of starlight reflecting off glass. Detecting the wake of a ship meant you were too late.

Still, sailors in the United States Navy found the four destroyers and fired thirty torpedoes into the darkness. None struck their targets. Even though the battle raged, none of the fifteen PT boats were damaged either.

The boats that had fired all their torpedoes were ordered back to base for more. Kennedy still had torpedoes, so his PT-109 rendezvoused with the PT-162 and the PT-169 to form a makeshift line across Blackett Strait. Idling around in the dark slowly to reduce noise and telltale wakes, they peered into the pitch-black night, looking and listening for enemy ships.

Around 2:30 a.m., Kennedy's crew saw one of the other PT boats cruising toward their starboard side. In a moment, though, as the ship became more visible in the dim starlight, panic struck the crew. The Japanese destroyer *Amagiri* was headed directly toward them.

Too late, Kennedy tried to turn starboard to get into a position to fire a torpedo. The destroyer, twenty times larger, crashed into the PT-109, effectively sinking her, and kept going, as if the ship's crew hadn't even noticed the impact.

Most of the sailors were tossed into the sea, but some managed to remain at their stations, including Kennedy, who had bounced around inside the cockpit. The collision burst the fuel tank and sparked it afire. Kennedy immediately ordered the remaining crew to abandon ship to prevent them from being killed by an exploding torpedo. They all dived into the water.

Below deck, Engineer Patrick McMahon was badly burned by the ignited fuel, but he managed to escape the burning wreckage.

Then, the wake of the passing ship washed over the PT-109, extinguishing the fire. Kennedy ordered the men back to the wreckage. Some were injured, some were sickened by breathing fumes and/or swallowing fuel. Two, Harold Marney and Andrew Jackson Kirksey, were missing and presumed dead.

Once assembled, they climbed back aboard the wreckage, which was taking on water, and hoped that one of the other PT boats would happen upon them in time. The light of morning made it obvious that there were no other boats in the area. They could see an islet three or four miles away, so eventually, when the PT-109 rolled over and there wasn't enough of the ship exposed for everyone to cling to, Kennedy ordered his crew to swim to the islet.

Kennedy had been on the Harvard swim team. A naturally strong swimmer, he used a belt held in his teeth to tow the burned McMahon. Two of the sailors did not know how to swim at all. Knowing they had been drafted into the Navy, no one scoffed or cursed them. Instead, they were lashed to a piece of wreckage to keep them afloat while seven of their fellow sailors towed them.

Five hours later, the eleven survivors crawled onto a beach of the coral island named Plum Pudding. Not knowing the name of the islet at the time, they dubbed it Bird Island because all the leaves were covered in bird droppings.

Kennedy swam out into the channel to see if he could flag down a passing PT boat, but he had no success, and the effort nearly killed him when the current swept him away.

The person they decided was the next strongest swimmer was George Ross, whom Kennedy ordered to make the same swim the next day.

Back in Boston, the headlines had first proclaimed, "Son of Joseph Kennedy Missing in South Pacific." The next day's headlines stated, "All Hands Lost on Kennedy Son's PT-109." Family and friends mourned but were rightfully hopeful.

For days, some or all of Kennedy's crew would swim to other islands in search of fresh water and food. They finally found help from two ally islander scouts, Biuku Gasa and Eroni Kumana, who were island-hopping in a canoe. Kennedy etched a note into a green coconut and asked the two locals to deliver the message.

The crew was scattered on different islands by then, but in the early morning hours of August 8, the last of the surviving crew was plucked from the islands and returned to base.

Kennedy was branded a hero. He was not happy with the label and, in fact, thought quite the opposite because he had not reacted fast enough to torpedo the *Amagiri*, or even avoid her. He felt responsible for losing two crew members, so when people called him a hero, he was uncomfortable.

Some of Kennedy's crew were also ill at ease with the amount of attention he received. Perhaps even resentful. After all, they had gone through the same ordeal, yet their fathers were not politicians, so their names were barely mentioned.

1944, August 12, Boston

A year and a few days after Jack's PT-109 incident, Joe Kennedy Jr. was killed in a failed experimental bombing mission. The family's grief would continue unchecked, but almost immediately, Joe Kennedy Sr. altered his plans. He had been grooming his namesake to become a politician like himself and had assumed that Jack and Bobby would be riding their older brother's coattails.

Joe was not entirely content with the prospect of having the "sickly" son be the inheritor of the leadership role of the Kennedy family. But he pivoted and committed to the notion.

1953–1956, The White House

A presidential aide in a crisp white shirt, a black suit, and a gray tie stepped into a surprisingly bland waiting room of the White House. The room was filled with eyeball-searing cigar and cigarette smoke, which made the aide squint, but despite this hindrance, he politely and matter-of-factly engaged the CIA director.

“Mr. Dulles, President Eisenhower will see you now.”

One of three men, who had been waiting longer than usual, stood, crushed out a cigarette, and followed the aide to the Oval Office, even though he knew his way around the White House better than the aide did.

Dwight David “Ike” Eisenhower greeted Dulles at the door with a warm handshake. Slipping into the chair behind his unassuming desk, the president immediately began detailing new orders to start funding and organizing a Cuban revolution. The two men also discussed ways to begin funneling money surreptitiously to the anti-communist efforts in Vietnam, including supplying arms to, and training for, guerrillas in Laos and Cambodia.

Ike asked for assurances that no African Americans, Hispanics, or Asians (not the terms he used) would be assigned to either of these high-priority missions. He made it clear he would not trust anyone with the new assignments unless they were a Protestant white male, preferably from Texas.

Days later, on another nondescript afternoon, President Eisenhower asked Joseph Kennedy Sr. to contact his old mobster liquor contacts to hire “real, live, Chicago mobster hit men” to help assassinate Castro or remove him from power. This decision was made even as the CIA continued working on the separate plan to lead a Cuban revolution.

Neither Eisenhower nor Kennedy realized that in Chicago, "The Family" was engaged in serious efforts to either muscle in on some of the casino and prostitute profits in Cuba, or partner up with them in some manner. A revolution at this time would interfere with these entrepreneurial efforts. A retired Cleveland cop who had relocated to Chicago was the contact who accepted the administration's cash, but *The Family* had no real intention of carrying out the assassination. They took the money, put on a good show, and spent the money in ways that promoted government corruption. They laughed about the deception for years.

Even before *The Family* could spend all that taxpayer money, Eisenhower picked up his ringing phone one day and grunted a greeting. After listening for a few minutes, he began second-guessing himself. He pushed himself away from his desk, leaned back as far as he dared, closed his eyes, and drew in a long, luxurious breath scented with the soft leather of his chair. He continued to listen for another moment, shaking his head slowly.

Was SEATO a grave error in judgment?

When the president had teamed up with France, Great Britain, New Zealand, Australia, the Philippines, Thailand, and Pakistan, the Southeast Asia Treaty Organization had seemed necessary. Recently, it was justification for sending aid and providing state-of-the-art military training to the newly-established South Vietnamese Army.

Seeing no other choice, he ordered more troops sent to the vicinity around Vietnam, Laos, Cambodia, and Thailand. When his orders were confirmed, he hung up without another word.

Several months later, President Eisenhower and several of his senior staff sat in a semi-darkened room surrounding a brand new, state-of-the-art color television set, trying to watch the news.

"Turn it up," barked an irritated president, looking at the old man to his right.

The man picked up a futuristic-looking flashlight from the table between them and, muttering something under his breath, fumbled with the "confounded" thing until a beam of light shone right into the face of another man leaning in to get a better look. Blinking ridiculously to rounds of laughter from the others, the recipient of the bright beam of light leaned back, shooting a dirty look to everyone but the president. Recovering, he then tried to focus on the TV, but the light shined to a different corner and the channel changed.

A chorus of colorful curses filled the room.

"Give me that thing!" The gruffest voice of the bunch spoke peremptorily as he snatched the flashlight out of the fumbling hands. He pointed it at another corner of the television, causing the volume to increase to a level loud enough to make the attendees blink with each word of a blaring cereal commercial. The light was shined into another corner of the TV set, and the "blasted thing" turned off. The early wireless remote control was jerked from his hand as another old man attempted to operate the new technology correctly.

Shaking his head, Eisenhower stood and held out his hand, expecting the flashlight/remote, which was handed to him immediately. The president placed the remote on a coffee table, walked across the room, and turned the TV back on. After finding the right channel, he adjusted the volume using the manual controls. The youngest man in the room, a future president himself, laughed heartily, as he had not had a turn with the flashlight, but he stopped short after receiving a sharp look from the president.

On the television, Senator John F. Kennedy was questioning a witness during the televised Select Committee on Labor inquiry into suspected corruption by Teamsters Union President Dave Beck. All listened intently as the questioning turned to political campaign contributions. The latest witness, coached, but not obviously, rattled off answers that skirted all around the involvement of the Republican Party, although he never quite implicated anyone but Beck.

The Eisenhower administration was pleased to see that their witness was able to answer all of Kennedy's questions without exposing their illegal source of income. They were confident that they would be able to continue with the reelection campaign *and* count on large sums of money flowing from the pockets of unwitting union workers, who thought they were supporting Democratic Party candidates.

Eisenhower was indeed pleased, but he openly expressed an intense hatred for the young, spoiled Kennedy for trying so desperately to topple the president with something as underhanded as going after illegal campaign contributions. Everyone knew that Jack Kennedy's father was guilty of the same behavior. Repeatedly.

Behavior. Not crime.

"The spoiled Paddy even owes his own senate seat to illegal campaign funds!"

A few days later, Eisenhower ordered CIA Director Dulles to pursue assassination attempts on Castro's life. "The cur-dog loves cigars. Find a way to supply him with some particularly *potent* ones. Also, I'm sure he has alienated relatives who would jump at the opportunity to get even with him. Find them."

The same racist rules applied as before, with one exception. Eisenhower added that he wanted Cubans, and only Cubans, to carry out the actual assassination attempts. Trusted CIA operatives were to make the plans and provide whatever was necessary to achieve their goals, but he wanted Americans as far away as possible from the end point of the mission, to reduce the chances of anyone tracing any activities back to his administration.

1956, Late August, The Heart of Boston

Jack Kennedy not only lost his bid for the Democratic nomination for vice president on August 17, but less than a week later, in Newport, Rhode Island, Jack and Jackie's first child was stillborn. Months passed before they recovered.

1957, Gettysburg

Uncomfortably cold temperatures and about a foot of snow blanketed half of Pennsylvania. The conditions reminded Eisenhower of times spent in Europe during WWII, memories that made him a bit sullen. Despite his mood, laughter burst from the president during his visit to a toasty-warm classroom full of kids. Well-dressed fifth graders with polite manners and new textbooks delighted in reading aloud and sharing their opinions about the content or author.

Eisenhower found that the warmth of the classroom and the delightful children improved his mood. The young students thoroughly enjoyed the company of the president of the United States of America, as well. The effects of his visit played a significant role in the lives of many of them. Seeing firsthand that a bigger-than-life hero was just a person like themselves made most of the children realize, some sooner than others, that average people were able to achieve lofty goals.

Across town, on the wrong side of the railroad tracks, a classroom full of children, whose ages and grades varied considerably, read three to a book. The poorly heated school, hastily constructed in the late 1800s, allowed the wintry outside air to seep in through walls, floors, and wooden shingles. The students crowded together near the hall because no one wanted to sit in the corner of the room where they would feel the bitter cold. Their coats helped to some degree, but the students were still cold.

Through the window in the classroom door, the old, white-haired principal watched the students shiver from the cold. Next to him was the vice principal, younger, but still a seasoned sixty-eight. Both the men pulled double duty at the old school. The principal also served as the school's accountant, while the vice principal coached sports and P.E. Still, no matter how many extra hours and shifts they worked, their efforts did not warm the school enough to prevent their students' teeth from chattering.

As usual, when the two were out of earshot of the students, they made no effort to hide the heavy Southern accents they had learned as children in this very school.

This situation seemed different, though, as *they* were in charge now and responsible for looking after the students. When they were young enough to sit at those same desks, shivering in much the same way, they simply endured the weather because they didn't know anything else. Having experienced the misery of the cold firsthand, and knowing that it did not have to be this way, made *watching* the cold children even more miserable than *being* them.

The principal's grandfather had been a young slave in Georgia who had relocated to Baltimore after the Civil War, thinking that the people who had fought so hard for his freedom would welcome him into their city. He was mistaken. He realized that most of them had not known that the freed slaves would try to migrate north and take their jobs. His grandfather then moved from Baltimore to Gettysburg in the 1870s, where he met his future wife. Together, they helped organize and build this old school.

Shaking his head in disbelief, the vice principal, a third-generation graduate himself, vented some frustration. "When I told them they was readin' three to a book, the fool actually said, 'Well, that ought to help keep 'em plenty warm then, won't it?'"

"*Got* to be a way to warm this place up."

After a pause the vice principal continued. "Saddest part is, some of them are warmer here than they are in they own home."

The principal remained silent, deeply saddened by the cold children and the state of his beloved old school.

"I invited the head cracker anyway. I figured, you know, he in town and all. Why can't he come and see the children shivering for his own self?"

Both men continued to watch through the door until the vice principal's body shuddered with a chill that had burrowed into his bones. Parting ways, each attended to the multiple tasks required to keep the school functioning.

Meanwhile, Eisenhower became uncomfortably warm with children gathered all around him. He pretended to find everything they said and read fascinating, and the kids seemed to love him. Some of the students chatting with the president would grow up and realize that, in historic Gettysburg, children on one side of the train tracks received a mere subset of the education the ones on the other side of the tracks were getting, but few would care. Even fewer would do anything to change the situation. Some of the shivering students would return to their school to teach and unwittingly become part of a culture that stifled many a bright future.

Bigots and racists throughout the United States approved of Eisenhower's quiet attempts to resegregate institutions such as the military, the FBI, and the CIA. Specific groups of people, made up almost entirely of white males, were elated over these efforts and felt as though America was back on track. Some swore a solemn oath to do their part to prevent America from returning to previous administrations' attempts at desegregation.

Despite Eisenhower's obvious prejudices, he received, and unjustifiably retained for many years, a good civil rights reputation because of his reaction to a string of incidents in Little Rock, Arkansas.

A perpetual cycle may exist only if people allow it to continue feeding itself, yet somehow, cultures that undermined the futures of their own constituents seem to persist. The students in the old schoolhouse in Gettysburg picked up the heavy accents used by their teachers and principals and passed it on to their own children, who passed it on to theirs, with few improvements.

In the business world, the HR representatives in charge of hiring rarely employed people with noticeable regional accents, so the graduates of this Gettysburg school, and many others like it, often stayed close to home, which helped perpetuate this culture.

Back in the White House, a seething Eisenhower and his administration were provoked daily by the young, arrogant Kennedy. His efforts to topple a war hero from the presidency and undermine the Republican Party were relentless.

1957, Little Rock, The Eisenhower Administration

The president of the Arkansas chapter of the NAACP, Daisy Bates, had been waiting patiently for many months, but her patience was now exhausted. When the third anniversary of the 1954 Supreme Court ruling of Brown v. Topeka Board of Education rolled around and not a single step of the state's six-year integration plan had yet been taken, Bates decided to take it upon herself to execute the plan. She began a campaign that would initially become known as the "Little Rock Crisis."

Over a period of about four months, Bates organized fellow NAACP volunteers and employees, convincing them to scour the city for the best candidates to enroll in Little Rock's Central High School. Her goal was to find respectable African American families whose children could do well academically in an all-white school. She needed a good showing and did not pursue mediocre students. Bates wanted the Black community to put their best foot forward to show the world that African American children were indeed "worthy" of attending any school they wished to attend.

Bates never considered the fact that she might be putting these high school students in harm's way. At the very least, it would have been safe to assume that at least *some* of the white kids might abuse, both mentally and physically, those they saw as different. It was widely known that high school students are often malicious to new students, excluding anyone they considered to be outsiders. For some, this common problem was amplified because of the lessons of hatred, racism, and bigotry passed on from their parents, or society. Or both.

Bates' thoughts were consumed only with what she considered to be the greater good. She managed to persuade nine families to send their kids to the all-white school. Few people outside Little Rock remember the name Daisy Bates, but the collective nickname for the nine Black students, "The Little Rock Nine," remained newsworthy for years.

Governor Orval E. Faubus was aware of Bates' plans to enroll the students but didn't particularly mind if Black kids went to school with white kids. That would be the problems or good fortunes of a handful of children and a small number of parents (voters). He had a state to operate. His usual motivation for taking any action was based primarily on input from the financiers responsible for his elections and the elections of those who would support his efforts.

Early one morning, over coffee made too strong, one particularly influential financier whose daughter would be attending Central High School that year *suggested* that Faubus order the Arkansas National Guard to surround the school on the day of enrollment. Later that morning, after the second pot of strong coffee was gone, the governor of Arkansas openly defied a Supreme Court ruling by ordering the state's guardsmen to prevent the African American students from entering the school "in the name of peace." Over the ensuing days, when the black students attempted to enter the school to enroll, they were turned away by state guardsmen.

When it became obvious that the problem was not going to resolve itself by one side or the other backing down, national government entities began putting pressure on the Arkansas administration to resolve the situation.

Finally, even though he was vacationing in Newport, Rhode Island, Eisenhower made time to meet with Faubus, who almost immediately agreed to allow the African Americans to enroll and attend school—as long as the guardsmen were allowed to remain in place to keep the peace. Eisenhower knew that the Arkansas governor had backed down and agreed far too easily. Before Faubus was on the plane back to Little Rock, he began planning the next escalation steps.

The students tried to enroll again, but once again were denied access by the guardsmen, "to keep the peace," because mobs of protesting whites were present.

After over three weeks of protests and failed enrollment attempts by the students, Eisenhower, keen to alleviate the mounting bad press, reluctantly federalized the Arkansas National Guard and took command of the troops. The commanding officer, Edwin A. Walker, a World War II and Korean War veteran, also happened to be a native of Texas, so Eisenhower trusted him. Still, to help ensure that all the *other* guardsmen complied with his orders, he also sent in a thousand paratroopers from the famed 101st Airborne Division for yet another "tailgate jump."

Even the worst of the white supremacists recognized that Eisenhower had no choice but to respond as he did. Nearly everyone either forgave him for his handling of the crisis or appreciated his efforts. Eisenhower's timing was nearly perfect. The American public generally felt he waited long enough for the problem to resolve itself, but when it did not, and with the eyes of the world upon him, they knew he had to act. All but the most extreme of the intolerant had grown weary of the continued problems in Little Rock and just wanted the blatant racism to go away, as *decent* people had wanted from the beginning.

1959, March 24, Washington, DC

No longer a young hoodlum engaging in petty crimes, Calogero Minacore, a.k.a. Carlos Marcello, had become quite the mob boss in New Orleans. He was in partial control of most of the casinos in the New Orleans area and had also forged mob ties in several other cities. "Business" relationships with real estate brokers in Florida were sufficiently profitable to justify even more time in prison, should that become necessary.

An occasional stint in prison was simply part of the lifestyle he had chosen. Marcello had already been incarcerated twice in state penitentiaries for assault, armed robbery, and trafficking marijuana.

Back in Washington, DC, John F. Kennedy had convinced his fellow Senate Committee members to use his brother, Robert F. Kennedy, as chief counsel, and together they were questioning Marcello about his activities and those of his associates. The inquiry focused on questionable behavior involving several business deals. Too many honest people had complained about his unfair business practices for years.

Smirking and pleading the Fifth Amendment, Marcello refused to answer any questions about his activities, his background, or anything about his associates. On the surface, the gangster seemed to enjoy toying with the United States senators, but internally he was furious about being ordered to be there. He had grown accustomed to being the one issuing orders, so he did not take the inquiry into his illegal activities lightly.

The Kennedy brothers were more frustrated than furious. They had also grown accustomed to those they opposed submitting to their wishes, fearful of the Kennedy family's power and influence. Privately, they agreed to sever Marcello from the fortunes his illegal activities had earned him over the years. They felt certain that only *Irish* organized crime had a place in

America, and that the Italian “Family” was barbaric, untrustworthy, and in the end, had to be displaced, one mobster at a time.

The smirk on Marcello’s face faded to a hint of satisfaction as he plotted a newsworthy fate for the Kennedys.

1960, September 26, Chicago

Jack Kennedy and Richard Nixon, colleagues from the U.S. Congress, met on television for the first nationally televised presidential debate. Jack looked good, but Nixon constantly wiped sweat from his face, grimacing from the pain of recent knee surgery. The bright stage lighting made him perspire profusely, and he was unable to stand still.

JFK's problematic back was bothering him somewhat as well, but only those who knew him well were able to ascertain he was in pain. Nixon's knee was tormenting him. He winced every time he shifted his weight. The presidential candidate, who would someday be known as "Tricky Dick," looked so bad that Mayor Daley ended a flabbergasted rant with, "...they've embalmed him before he even died!" While Kennedy presented himself as smooth and confident, he wouldn't have appeared so had he not taken the amphetamines Dr. Max Jacobson had given him just minutes before they went on the air.

In Nixon's opinion, Kennedy was making him look bad, which angered him more and more as the debate dragged on, in part because Nixon had planned to do the same to Kennedy. Nixon was annoyed, and although this did not affect his keen debating abilities, his demeanor revealed his irritation increasingly as the debate wound down. Nixon's choice for vice president, Henry Cabot Lodge Jr., shook his head in disgust. In the debate's waning moments, as the candidates were making closing arguments, Lodge correctly predicted to no one in particular, "That son of a bitch just lost the election!"

After the debate, after all the cameras had been turned off, Nixon was openly angry and agitated, cursing loudly and blasting Kennedy for being a young, smart-ass kid. Then his anger shifted and he chastised himself for losing the debate, which was one of many wrong assumptions that would haunt his political career. A large number of people who saw the debate on television thought that JFK won the debate. However, the significantly larger audience who had listened to the debate on the radio believed that Nixon had won.

With several witnesses present who heard him clearly, Nixon swore a solemn oath to get even with the so-and-so, no matter what and no matter how long it took.

1960, Four Days in November

A new four-door sedan, dusty from the road but otherwise looking out of place, rolled through a Chicago alley, crunching over broken glass and flattening pieces of trash. The car stopped a few feet from the side door of a nightclub, effectively blocking the alley, and the two men inside looked around.

The driver, who was a few noticeable years older than the passenger, reached behind the seat and picked up a metal lockbox from the back floorboard. They looked up and down the alley again, nodded to each other as only amateur criminals would, exited the car in unison, and walked briskly through the nightclub's door.

They did not remove their hats once inside, as they normally would. In fact, when a half-naked young waitress bounced up to them, the passenger pulled his brim down a little further over his eyes. The server pressed the bare skin of her torso up against the older man, as only a woman with plenty of such experience would, and whispered something in his ear. Looking him in the eye, she waited for a nod, then walked off.

Despite it being too early in the day for customers, there were two groups of men sitting at tables across a large dance floor from each other. In one group, everyone was leaning back in their chairs away from each other, as if they were all keeping a watchful eye on one another. (They were.) They talked about nothing while waiting on their cohorts across the dance floor to complete their business.

The other group was smaller, and everyone was leaning in, heads close to one another, voices barely audible. One of the men in this group, dressed considerably more uptown than the others, looked sternly into each of their eyes as he addressed them. They studiously avoided his glare.

The bartender handed the waitress a tray of drinks at the bar, and she carried them to this smaller, quieter table. The two men with the lockbox stood silently by the door, watching her with growing impatience. A long, uncomfortable wait followed. As she handed each of the men in the group a drink, she paused long enough to whisper something into the ear of the well-dressed stern one, who looked over his shoulder at the two, locking eyes with the older man. The long, hard, mean stare caused the entire room to lapse into silence.

Attempting not to appear intimidated, the older man stared back, but the younger of the two whispered through clenched teeth, “We don’t have to put up with this. Let’s—”

“Shut up!” The older man interrupted with a voice and demeanor the younger man had never witnessed before. “You’ll get us shot, stabbed, and buried alive somewhere.”

The younger man trembled inwardly but dared not show it.

Still staring, the well-dressed man at the table had made everyone in the room uncomfortable. The men on the other side of the dance floor watched intently, hands on the grips of their pistols.

Finally, to everyone’s relief, the well-dressed man waved the two newcomers with the lockbox over to his table. Somehow, he even managed to make the wave appear intimidating. Each hand or eye movement had meaning, no matter how slight, with the latest one being a signal for three of the other five men at his table to leave.

They stood without question or hesitation and joined the men at the other table where the most charismatic of them slapped another on the back, spewing barnyard language. The others joined in, poking fun at each other’s attire or choice of haircut, subconsciously allowing pressure to escape through humor. The highly charged tension of the previous few moments had affected them more than they realized. Thugs with guns would always find an outlet.

The well-dressed man seemed to become disproportionately larger and more threatening as the two nervous newcomers approached. One of the other two remaining men at the table with slicked-back hair and an expressionless face moved his hand to the grip of the pistol stuffed into the waistband of his pants. He remained calm and quiet, but his complete lack of expression made him appear menacing. The other man was so meek he appeared to be out of place, and he avoided eye contact as the newcomers approached. The shirt under his old jacket was wrinkled as though he had slept in it, and his tie was loose and crooked.

"You gotta problem, kiddo?" The thick mobster-style Chicago accent made the big brute seem even more dangerous.

The younger, terror-stricken man, still trying to keep his eyes hidden behind the brim of his hat, managed to steel his nerves enough to answer with a steady voice, although with an obvious defensive tone.

"There's no problem."

Turning his attention to the older man, he barked, "Gimme the box."

As directed, the older of the two tried to hand the lockbox to the well-dressed man, who made no effort to reach for it. Instead, he glanced impatiently at the man with slicked-back hair, who released the grip he had on his pistol and took possession of the box with a rude jerk. They both reached into their pockets and produced keys, but the slick-haired man's key ring was far bigger than the older man's set.

The gangster looked at the lock, scrutinizing it closely, then searched through his enormous set and selected three adjoining keys. The second one opened the lockbox. The two newcomers, still wearing their hats, looked at each other in subdued astonishment. The older man pocketed his keys as the three men at the table peered into the lockbox.

"They in there?"

"Yeah, boss."

"You know what to do."

Slick-haired man hurried off with the box, and at the snap of mean fingers, the other sheepish man with the wrinkled shirt pulled an envelope from a breast pocket and handed it to the older hatted man, who slipped it into his own breast pocket. The younger man looked at his partner, clearly upset that he had not counted the money, but he received very different looks from the older man and the well-dressed gangster.

Before the situation could turn ugly, the slick-haired man interrupted them by returning the lockbox. Without wasting a second, the older man retrieved the box, noticing immediately that it was heavier, and headed straight for the door, partner in tow. They scrambled into their car and sped away from the bar, each equally eager to get as far from the mob as one could while remaining in Chicago.

The next day, in Austin, it was too hot to be early November. Two transplant Texans waited in a 1959 Eldorado with huge, ridiculous fins. The man in the driver's seat kept glancing at his watch. "How long should we wait?"

The passenger shook his head, said, "Hell if I know," and tried to find something besides twangy country music and static on the radio.

Eventually, a loud, rusty old two-door Ford with Louisiana plates pulled into the parking lot and cruised up alongside them. The Texans handed three metal boxes through their car windows to a sweaty New Orleans thug who opened each box, replaced the contents of each, and then passed them back. Tucked into the handle of the last box was a bulging envelope. Both vehicles drove away without a single word being exchanged.

While cruising down a brand-new Interstate, the passenger of the finned car split the contents of the envelope, stuffed his cut into his back pocket, and handed the remainder to the driver. Unable to look each other in the eye or even speak to each other during the drive to the official ballot-counting headquarters, they delivered the drop boxes as though nothing out of the ordinary had happened. The guilty silence between the two lasted for the remainder of the time they were friends, which wasn't much longer.

Two days later, in a seedy, smoky New Orleans strip club in the middle of a bright sunny afternoon, the same sweaty thug who had been in Austin met with a man who wore too much gaudy jewelry to be seen in such a dive on a regular basis. They shamelessly replaced hundreds of pieces of paper in another lockbox in full view of the patrons of the bar, the topless waitresses, and the nude strippers on a stage within an arm's reach of their table. In the area of town once commonly referred to as Little Italy, but now widely known as the French Quarter, no one seemed to care about the illegal activities happening in plain view.

Finishing the illicit task, the jewelry-laden man slammed the lockbox closed, threw down a stiff drink, and, after slamming down the empty glass with an exaggerated sigh, rushed out of the back door with one final slam.

A Boston newspaper headline proclaimed, "Kennedy Defeats Nixon in Nation's Closest Race for Presidency."

Americans were blissfully ignorant of the organized efforts of illegal activities that helped elect John F. Kennedy to the White

House. To many of them, this new day seemed as if it could last a lifetime.

In a perverse way, they were correct.

1961, January, Washington, DC

One of the last things Eisenhower did before leaving office was to officially break off formal political relations with Cuba and Fidel Castro. He did not want anyone to interfere with the long-term plans he and the CIA had made. The investment had been significant, and if future presidents or members of congress stopped the operation, that would also make him look bad.

He felt that the mission against Castro must continue, right or wrong. The next president would have to deal with the aftermath, as he had so carefully planned. The Cuban invasion would be in the final stages of the "training phase" when he left office.

"Allen, concerning Cuba, let nothing deter our efforts. *Nothing*. Not political pressure, nor other high priorities, nor *future presidents*. Castro and his red *com*rades *have* to go if we want to preserve our precious but fragile American way of life." The most successful general of the second-most important war ever fought on planet Earth overemphasized his words to stress their consequential gravity.

CIA Director Allen Welsh Dulles listened closely, taking the words to heart, even though he realized that the day of the invasion had conveniently been planned for April 1961, long after the next president was scheduled to take office. His fellow CIA agents were training Cuban exiles and rebels in Guatemala, but as the day of the invasion drew nearer, the trainees became increasingly more uncomfortable with the bold plan.

When John F. Kennedy took office, Dulles' loyalty remained with Eisenhower, possibly due to political party affiliation. Dulles lied to Kennedy about the Cuban operation, exaggerating his confidence and downplaying the resistance American forces would likely encounter. Such resistance, Dulles well knew, would be considerable, as Castro had abundant small-arm firepower at his disposal, courtesy of the USSR, and was eager to control a strategic position so close to the United States.

Planners failed to plan thoroughly, reconnaissance was practically nonexistent, and even though the invasion of Cuba was a large military operation, only the CIA was involved in training the Cuban rebels. This preparation continued for several weeks into Kennedy's term, during which he was given only good news and nothing that might indicate that the mission should be pulled back or rescaled. Meanwhile, the new president authorized the continuation of assassination attempts on Castro's life.

1961, January 25, The White House

Evelyn Lincoln, the long-time presidential secretary, answered as many phone calls as she could for the new president and logged them into the official call log. Typically, she enjoyed speaking with each caller, who could be from anywhere in the United States, or even the world. One call she received on January 15 was a little different from most calls and was the only one that made her uncomfortable.

There was a certain amount of instability in Marguerite Oswald's voice as she insisted that President Kennedy needed to do something to help her son, Lee. She claimed that Soviet agents had coerced him into signing defection papers. She went on to say that her son had been in the Marines and was a true patriot. Mrs. Oswald swore there was no way Lee would have signed defection papers unless someone had forced him to do so.

After Mrs. Oswald had repeated herself a few times, Lincoln ended the phone call by hanging up on her in mid-sentence. The devoted secretary recorded the call into the phone log and moved on to the next call.

Kennedy never saw the message.

1961, February, Miami, Florida

A puzzled Edward Rickenbacker read a letter from Arcacha Smith, a Cuban Revolutionary Council (CRC) activist. Rickenbacker, the Eastern Air Lines chairman of the board and ex-president and CEO, could not fathom why Smith was requesting a *paid* sixty- to ninety-day leave of absence for one of their pilots, David Ferrie, so he could work full-time for the CRC.

It took only a couple of phone calls to discover that Ferrie had a troubled employment history with Eastern Air Lines from the very beginning. He had been reprimanded several times during his relatively short employment, and *two* of those investigations were still in progress. Yet despite the negative reports, the Eastern Air Lines HR department insisted that his file also contained numerous compliments and high praise from both his superiors and his peers.

A note in Ferrie's HR file also caused Rickenbacker to pause. An investigator pointed out that all his fellow pilots agreed that even though Ferrie was a bit odd at times, he was highly competitive and an excellent pilot.

One factor made Rickenbacker's choice clear when he read that one of the open investigations, and several of the reprimands, revolved around activities with underage high school boys, often runaways or other troubled young men.

Disgusted, Rickenbacker wadded the letter tightly and tossed it into the trash.

1961, March, Near Puerto Cabezas

A mosquito-netted helmet blurred a beautiful view of a perfectly blue Caribbean Sea, but the "newbie" CIA agent did not dare take off his protective gear. The Nicaraguan mosquitoes were *relentless*. If he were to remove the uncomfortable headpiece, he knew his face and neck would soon have as many red welts as his hands and wrists, which were exposed out of necessity.

The native Nicas didn't seem to mind the mosquitoes, but the American's milky white skin attracted the hungry little females from miles around. The other agents, hardened from years of experience in the field, had given him a malodorous lotion that was supposed to repel the voracious little creatures. Still, it seemed that the ointment was not a repellant at all, but an attractant. Someone's misguided idea of a joke?

To keep his mind off the torturous stinging and itching, he began hypothesizing theories about why the mosquitoes were not responding to the best the CIA and Berkeley had to offer in the form of insect repellant. Perhaps the research that went into producing the product focused exclusively on mosquitoes in the United States, but the ones found here in the palm groves of Nicaragua were a different species. Different enough for the repellant to be completely ineffective.

Perhaps he was sweating so much from the heat and humidity that the chemicals meant to repel the tiny monsters had long since trickled away with his perspiration. Or maybe they were more drawn to him than the natives because his skin hadn't become hardened to the mosquito's microscopic, needle-like suckers. He wondered if the Aggies at Texas A&M could make a better repellant.

Loud strings of curses and newly phrased profanity sprayed spit and hatred from between his clenched teeth as a mosquito found its way into the netted helmet. It buzzed his ear and then an eye. He ripped the netted helmet off his hot, sweaty head and continued to curse louder and louder as a swarm of wings and needles ignored his frantically waving arms and hands.

Several natives looked on with quiet and calm interest, amazed at the mosquitoes' unnatural attraction to the *Americano's* pale skin. Two of them were making little attempt to hide their amusement, and they sneered at the CIA agent with contempt and disrespect. It was painfully obvious that the Nicaraguans didn't care about the man at all and that they would all prefer it if the Americans packed up and went home. The mosquitoes, on the other hand, were enjoying the company of this particular human.

Just as the newbie was about to lose all control, an impatient and weathered American grabbed him by the arm and escorted him to a nearby makeshift shower, pushing him under the nozzle, turning on the water for him. The agent experienced instant relief from his agony and quickly regained his composure. Just in time, too. He thought he might go insane without some relief.

Not wasting a single word, the officer showed the new field agent how to don his equipment properly to keep the mosquitoes on the outside of his gear. Together, they joined another CIA agent and several Nicas who were painting over the USA insignia of an old B-26 Marauder. Various other planes were in the immediate vicinity, some still adorned with the markings of the United States Air Force or Army, while others had fresh Cuban insignia painted to appear aged and slightly worn.

Standing in the semi-shade of the World War II surplus camouflage netting spread over the planes, which provided cover for the cameras in Soviet spy planes far above them, the newbie shook his head in disbelief. He was barely able to contain his contempt. "So, whose idea was this?"

"Dulles."

"Mmm." Nodding now, the recent graduate was also using a sarcastic inflection that irritated the senior agent. "Straight from the top. I see at least a dozen planes here—"

"Sixteen."

"Yeah, so, isn't it widely known in most intelligence circles that Castro only has about that many planes in his entire air force?"

A simple nod indicated an affirmative answer, and one did not need the body language training they both had been given to read the experienced agent's facial expressions. Anyone could tell he knew where the newbie was going with his point, but that didn't prevent the young field agent from continuing.

"Sooo, who's going to believe that Castro's entire air force has defected?"

The older agent had always been a man with little to say, but when he spoke, people listened, and what he said, people understood. This time, it was only two simple, stabbing words sheathed in sarcasm. "The press."

"Well, maybe the A teams will get him first."

A half-startled look from a nearby Nicaraguan named Julio made it apparent that he understood English better than he had disclosed, and a stern look from a very hard man made the newbie wish he'd kept his mouth shut, even out here in the wilds of Central America. The training he had received had pounded it into his head that letting something slip out is far easier than anyone ever anticipated, and now he realized why they spent so much time trying to prepare him and his classmates for instances such as this.

A potential hostile now had confirmation that assassins were trying to kill Castro. Not only had the newbie made this serious blunder, he had also let slip something as simple as "A team," referring to assassins. Now the Nicaraguans knew that they were not even part of the *Americanos'* main plan to free Cuba. It didn't take long for word to get to the other Nicas, and some of them wondered how expendable they were.

With a better understanding of why the hardened officer spoke so few words, the new field agent tried his best to keep his educated but opinionated mouth shut the rest of the day. Truly feeling like the newbie that the other agents had given him a hard time about, he knew now that the fewer words he spoke, the better the agent he would become. He reluctantly accepted his nickname, "Newbie."

After another long, sweaty, sleepless night spent swatting and rearranging netting, the morning rays seemed comforting. However, while Newbie was donning his mosquito attire before attempting to venture off his cot and out of the netting, he became aware of a minor commotion outside his tent. Nicas were milling about, talking amongst themselves. Questioning a translator, he learned they were wondering where Julio had gone. Some were cursing various gods and other menacing entities.

Newbie was stunned. He knew exactly what had happened. The words that slipped out of his mouth had gotten Julio killed. The hardened officer he respected yesterday looked as if he had not missed a wink of sleep, and he somehow looked even harder as he sipped his morning coffee with no show of emotion.

1961, Cuba

(Exact locations and dates are lost to history.)

Near Guantanamo Bay on a typically warm, balmy night, a Cuban accepted a duffle bag from two "A team" CIA agents. He immediately unzipped the bag to reveal a large caliber semi-automatic pistol and four full clips crowning several stacks of American fifty-dollar bills.

The Cuban's nostrils flared as he contemplated snatching up the pistol and killing the Americans. He imagined putting his hand in the bag, switching off the safety, and shooting at the CIA agents until he was out of bullets.

His perverse, fleeting fantasy included a life of hiding afterward and eventually being discovered by the relentless CIA while on his new houseboat docked in a cozy Cuban cove. He then imagined what life would be like as a rich man in America, surrounded by beautiful women who lusted after him and his money. The thought of powerful men answering to him and calling him "sir" was nearly as appealing as his fantasy of swarms of half-naked women, so when he reached into the bag, instead of grabbing the pistol, he grabbed a handful of money and began counting it.

Like most people, his greed influenced his behavior more than his hatred or prejudices.

"We don't have time for you to count all that. Half the money is there. Take it or leave it," hissed the agent who had handed him the bag. "You'll get the other half when Castro is confirmed dead."

The Cuban spouted a hushed barrage of Spanish insults. When the spooks responded with nothing but cold stares, the Cuban scurried away into the night. The CIA agents never heard from him again.

1961, Miami Beach

(Exact locations and dates are lost to history.)

A Cuban refugee living in a predominantly Cuban housing project accepted fifty thousand American dollars to contact his cousin in Cuba, whom he insisted *hated* Castro. The CIA also knew that the Cuban's cousin was one of Castro's closest advisors. The agents checked back often, albeit on an irregular schedule, to see if the Cuban's cousin was willing to cooperate with the CIA. After a week and a half of phone calls, the Miami Beach resident still reported that he had not heard back from his cousin in Cuba.

One day the refugee did not answer his phone. After several hours of failed attempts to reach him, the CIA sent agents to check on the family. The house was empty except for some insignificant objects left scattered about on the floors.

Indicative of a hasty evacuation, trash remained in the kitchen wastebasket, a load of wet towels in the washing machine was beginning to mildew, and items were left in the freezer. The family had disappeared, and it was difficult to determine whether they had left willingly or had been forcibly removed.

Over a cheap brunch at the airport, the two federal agents from DC argued about whether or not they should have maintained a twenty-four-hour watch over the family. After a brief lull in the heated discussion, the argument turned to deciding which underling would take the heat for wasting yet *another* fifty grand of the CIA's dwindling tactical budget. The Chief of Psychological Warfare Operations in Miami, George Joannides, was going to be disappointed.

1961, Key Largo

(Exact locations and dates are lost to history.)

On a pristine Key Largo beach, a squinting CIA field agent and a Cuban known to have an older half-brother close to Castro were trying to blend in with the tourists but were failing miserably. The sound of waves, wind, seagulls, and people playing in the water prevented their conversation from drifting to unwanted ears, but the Cuban was still looking around nervously. At the urging of the agent, who was not a fan of unwanted attention, the Cuban took a deep breath of warm, salty air, but it didn't help. The anxiety continued to build.

"My brother would leap at the chance of taking Castro out of the photograph, for everyone hates that lying bastard."

The agent looked at him for a moment, considered correcting the Cuban's translation, but decided to let it go. They began negotiating instead. He would need a large sum of cash and new identities for his entire family. Both points were agreed upon after some haggling. As they discussed details about how to get instructions to the half-brother, a fair-sized pleasure boat pulled in closer to shore but turned around before it got too close to the sandy beach.

As the agent asked where he and his family might want to move, part of the Cuban's head exploded and he collapsed into an awkward heap. The agent hit the beach and tried to squirm his way deep into the sand. In a few moments, he eased his head up to look for the shooter and more substantial cover than sand and a dead body. The moment he saw a high-powered rifle pointing at him from the pleasure boat's stern, he took a shot to the forehead.

While a crowd gathered around the bodies, the driver of the pleasure boat cruised away in a manner that did not draw attention.

1961, Havana

(Exact locations and dates are lost to history.)

A CIA operative in a dingy hotel room was talking to "Manuel," one of the hotel's employees, the conversation consisting only of tourist and casino information. However, an entirely different and simultaneous conversation was taking place on a sheet of hotel stationery. Scribbled notes passed back and forth between them as though there were a possibility that the room was bugged or that someone was in the next room listening.

The CIA agent knew no one was within earshot and that no listening devices were in the room. He also knew how to take advantage of the average person's need to feel important or an essential part of a grim, secret government plot. The Cuban agreed to take out Castro, claiming that getting into the kitchen wouldn't be any problem as he was the hotel restaurant's assistant manager and was in and out of the kitchen several times a day.

While they were engaged in both conversations, the agent pulled a unique cigarette lighter out of his pocket and showed Manuel how to pull it apart to get to the packet of designer toxins. On a fresh piece of paper, the agent wrote, "Be very careful with this—do not get any of it on your hands."

As Manuel read the latest note, the agent asked in broken Spanish where he might find a cantina where the Cuban maidens might be especially friendly.

While scribbling another note, Manuel also pretended to explain how to get to a brothel a few blocks away. The agent returned another note while verbally thanking him. Once the agent was sure that the minion fully understood the plan and was relatively confident that Manuel was indeed capable of assassinating Castro, he gave him a suitcase with too much money in it.

His mission complete, the CIA operative went down to the hotel casino, where he spent the next two days gambling, partying, and visiting some of those friendly Cuban maidens that Manuel had told him how to find. "Undercover perks." The justification was simple: if you wanted to look like a tourist, you were obligated to act like a tourist. And there were still many people vacationing in Cuba, despite the wishes of the United States government.

Castro finally showed up at the hotel a half day late. He and several elite Cuban soldiers went upstairs to a corner of the restaurant on the top floor, which overlooked a small river with banks lined with lush, flowering tropical plants. The occasional, colorful tropical bird could be spotted between trees, and fishermen tossed nets out into the river from boats so weathered they shouldn't have been floating. Soon, choking cigar smoke filled the café, partially obscuring the scenery. To anyone who did not know who they were, the men would have appeared comical as they sucked on their huge cigars.

Through the small window in the kitchen door, Manuel peered out into the dining area where Castro's boisterous laugh radiated arrogance. The would-be assassin's knees weakened and his hands trembled. He repeatedly used the back of his thumb to wipe away nervous beads of sweat that returned persistently within seconds.

He had not realized how intimidating Castro was in person. Manuel was all but frozen from fear. Castro could, and would, if he sensed evil intentions, have Manuel and his entire family tortured.

The vile compound that could end Castro's life remained in Manuel's pocket. Although there were several opportunities to mix the poison into their dinner throughout the evening, Manuel could not find the courage to follow through. Even before Castro finished his hearty meal, the would-be assassin tossed the cigarette lighter out of the window onto an accumulating trash heap behind the hotel.

Castro's brutal intimidation tactics had saved his life yet again.

When the CIA agent saw Castro leaving the hotel, he briefly considered slitting Manuel's throat, but did not. They still might be able to use him in the future.

1961, Farmland in Cuba

All over Cuba, repeated over and over and over...

Billows of black smoke rose above flames too intense to be a naturally occurring fire. Having started in one corner of the sugarcane field, which also happened to be upwind, the wind forced the flames to consume the entire crop. As the fire spread rapidly and the accelerant burned off, the smoke turned from black to grey. The two-year crop, due to be harvested in less than a week, was reduced to ashes in a matter of minutes, along with the hopes of farmers trying to provide for their families.

Old, inferior Soviet farm equipment plowed the burned fields and replanted the sugarcane as though there were a chance that the next crop would mature and get harvested before the CIA's hired hands burned their fields again.

1961, April 4, New Orleans & Guatemala

After weeks of legal preparation by Bobby Kennedy, and careful consideration of repercussions by much of the administration, Jack Kennedy issued an arrest warrant for Carlos Marcello. Not trusting the corrupt New Orleans authorities, Bobby had federal agents arrest Marcello while he was checking in at the Immigration Services Office, as required by law for all illegal aliens.

Before Marcello could contact an attorney or even tell his family that he was apparently going to be gone for a while, he was on a plane bound for an unknown destination. He knew only that *someone* was having him deported *somewhere*. Within seconds of landing, he realized he was in Guatemala City.

Guatemala!

Shortly after he had started using his "Carlos Marcello" alias when he was a young child organizing teen gangs, he had begun building an elaborate cover story to accompany the assumed name. Now older, his alternate identity well established, he avoided discussing his past as much as possible so he didn't have to remember all the lies he'd told over the years.

Those lies included details about how he and his family had migrated from Guatemala when he was young. In reality, he had never been to Central America, despite having a fake Guatemalan passport and a 1953 birth certificate from San José Pinula.

During the weeks he was there, Marcello took advantage of the situation, meeting with his produce and marijuana "business partners." He did his best to appear as though he were enjoying the Guatemalan sights under the ever-present eyes of the CIA. However, the gangster was angrier than he had ever been in his life. And he was typically angry most of the time.

Being away from "business" for more than a few hours was bad enough, but going for days without monitoring his people could easily cost him *thousands* of dollars, possibly allowing others to muscle in on the hundreds of illegal opportunities he had leveraged over the past few decades.

Secret Service and CIA agents constantly harassed Marcello and his family, who had joined him at the Biltmore Hotel in Guatemala City. Exasperated by the thought of Marcello turning the "deportation" into a vacation, the Feds eventually arranged to have him and his attorney, Mike Maroun, dropped off in the middle of a jungle in Honduras. A jungle! They barely survived.

While in Central America, and long after returning home, the Italian American made countless threats toward the Kennedys. The threats continued for many months while the seething anger slowly became more of a desire for revenge. He simply could not let the deportation incident go unpunished. Whenever someone mentioned politics, Marcello ranted about Bobby Kennedy, even during business meetings.

In one such meeting, a shady businessman named Edward Becker listened to a typical tirade during which Marcello used the phrase usually reserved for ordering a hit, "Take the stone from my shoe." He also looked Becker in the eyes and told him that a dog would keep biting you if you cut off only its tail, but if you cut off its head, the dog would die. It was clear to Becker that by "tail," Marcello meant Bobby, and by "head," he meant Jack.

1961, April 7, The USA & Guatemala

The *New York Times* reported that Cuban exile revolutionary guerrillas were being trained in Guatemala, Florida, and Louisiana by American military personnel for what was correctly assumed to result in a Cuban invasion.

This was supposed to be a clandestine operation. *Co*vert, not *o*vert. One would have thought that the head of the Central Intelligence Agency, or *someone*, would have informed the president of the United States that the element of surprise had been severely compromised. Too many people failed to offer alternate courses. Kennedy's trust in them was naïve.

Neither of these things happened. Dulles continued to march straight down the path the previous president had shown him, and he tried to convince a handful of reporters that there was no truth to the stories.

Dulles' fierce loyalty to Eisenhower likely played a significant role in one of the biggest blunders in American history.

1961, April 15, Near Puerto Cabezas

No longer feeling quite like the newbie that his fellow agents still all-too-frequently reminded him of, the agent watched eight of the sixteen bombers roar overhead as only planes heavily loaded with armament could. His demeanor was solemn, however—typical of someone watching his comrades and accomplices parade off toward an uncertain fate during uncertain times.

Even though all eight planes returned sooner than expected, with no CIA or Cuban rebel casualties or injuries, his mood remained somber. He was less entrenched in the operation than his fellow operatives, who had been involved in Nicaragua for many months. The newbie had a unique, disengaged vantage point about the entire concept.

He was neither impressed with the operation nor confident that their efforts would succeed. The agent had tried voicing his concerns about the plan, particularly the ridiculously elaborate ruse (already underway) that he believed was doomed to fail. He had been told that the mission would continue unless the new president of the United States canceled it, which seemed unlikely.

To make matters worse, the newbie had the unpleasant task of informing the crews of the bombers that their new orders were to stand down. Their planes would not be refueled, and they would not be allowed to return to finish the job they had barely started. This order meant that their invasion force, already en route via the Caribbean Sea, would meet air resistance, an eventuality they were neither prepared for nor equipped to handle.

The Cuban ambassador to the United Nations, not fooled for a moment, denounced the attack on Cuban soil as a shameless act of aggression by the United States. His hatred for the United States was apparent as his rage hissed through clenched teeth.

Adlai Ewing Stevenson II, former governor of Illinois and newly appointed U.S. ambassador to the United Nations, stood at the prestigious U.N. podium assuring the assembly—and the entire world—that the United States had nothing to do with the attack on Cuba just hours before. Many listeners believed Stevenson, for he had worked hard to earn the reputation of being a good, honest man and had striven even harder to maintain such an esteemed status among the citizens of the world.

A single B-26 bomber marked with Cuban insignia made an emergency landing in Florida. The waiting press hounds, hungry for news about the attack on Cuba, devoured the pilot's story of his mission and took numerous pictures of the bullet holes in the plane's fuselage. A couple of the reporters who had spent some time covering the "police action" in Korea gazed at the holes, wondering how so much small-arms fire had managed to hit the craft at all, and all in one single removable panel.

One of the other more seasoned reporters asked the pilot why his gunner had not fired his machine guns, but the pilot had no clear answer. The Cuban defector stammered that he didn't understand English well enough to answer any more questions, and as more facts became public, more reporters grew suspicious.

Another reporter with adequate math skills wondered how a B-26 could have bombed Cuba and then flown over two hundred miles between the time the bombings were reported and the time the plane had arrived in Florida. He calculated that the cumbersome bomber would have had to reach and maintain speeds better than four hundred miles per hour to make the trip.

Pictures of the "defecting" pilot beside his aircraft circulated quickly, and, nearly as quickly, several veterans of WWII noticed that the nose of the aircraft was that of a B-26F, a later model of craft that had no forward machine gun at all, and therefore no Plexiglas nose. The Cuban B-26 bombers were widely known to be older models with front-mounted machine guns and an entire nose that the gunner could see through like a windshield.

The surprise attack destroyed or damaged much of Castro's small air force, but because the CIA and the rebels were not allowed to reload and return, over half of the Cuban Air Force was left intact and functional. Only seven Cubans had lost their lives, but many more sustained wounds.

Castro immediately unleashed his loyalists into the general population of "his" island, rounding up everyone he and his intelligence community thought might have supported a revolution. In the chaos and confusion, many took advantage of the situation to settle old scores. Others arrested or even killed people they considered competition for promotions or the affections of a woman.

Thousands of Cubans whom the loyalists perceived as a threat, or had *ever* been considered a threat, died or were jailed because the CIA bombed Castro's air force under the guise of a Cuban exile revolution. Consequently, all the Cuban rebels that the CIA's plan depended upon were dead, incarcerated, or had the fight frightened out of them.

1961, April 16, The United Nations

"Wayne? Adlai. I'm flying to Washington tomorrow to turn in my resignation to Jack."

"What? Why?" The Oregon senator was doing a fair job of pretending he didn't know why his friend of many years wanted to resign.

"Because no one will ever believe me again, and rightfully so! The entire world thinks I lied to them. I did not! Meet me at my place in Georgetown tomorrow and we'll talk."

"Just hold on now, Adlai. People don't resign from coveted positions like the U.S. ambassador to the United Nations over one dismal experience. Besides," Wayne Morse tried to interject a little humor into the situation to lighten the mood, as only a good friend would, "everyone will start calling you Egghead again."

This did get a little chuckle and a slow head shake from Stevenson, and he began to calm down, although he was still seething internally. They both also knew that Morse had no intentions of meeting Stevenson anywhere, but he did manage to talk him out of resigning.

However, Morse could not seem to quell Stevenson's intense hatred for John F. Kennedy. Adlai Stevenson had worked hard his entire life to maintain the reputation of being honest and virtuous. He had been a governor of Illinois! People thought of Chicago as being equivalent to The Mob, yet he defied all the bribery attempts and shunned every threat to maintain his constituents' trust. To Stevenson, President Kennedy destroyed that reputation as casually as someone crushing an ant beneath a shoe.

The loathing Stevenson felt for Kennedy exuded from every moral argument either of them had ever made and nearly consumed him. He felt his political career was over, and therefore his life was over as well, for all practical purposes. He was angry enough to have violent thoughts, which he had never had before, even when dealing with mobsters in Chicago. He never wanted any of those people dead, only imprisoned. But Kennedy? Stevenson imagined the world would be a better place if someone simply took the arrogant child out. If only he had the means and *any* chance of succeeding...

1961, April 16, Across the USA

People lived in constant fear of a nuclear war. Children had pointless nuclear attack drills during which they were instructed to get under their desks and cover the backs of their necks with their hands. All but the youngest understood that their desks and hands wouldn't stop the inferno of a nuclear blast. The drills did nothing but increase fear and anxiety.

Still, lives had changed for the better despite the threat of being incinerated in a split second. Less than twenty years after the unparalleled devastation of World War II, America was flourishing again, and life was generally better, thriving because so many good people fought for change, with many of them sacrificing their lives to help make the changes needed to maintain freedom.

But the fear of nuclear war and communism held hostage all those who were aware. It was a deep-rooted fear, and for good reason. The Soviet Union was doing much more than what people described as "saber-rattling." Threats materialized into actions all too often as they expanded their borders relentlessly, absorbing more and more of the peripheral territories in the area.

America was guilty of her fair share of intimidating behaviors as well. However, when new states joined the United States, it was their choice to do so. The promise of red dictators was real, and frightening, but the new states were not overthrown or absorbed against their will. The citizens voted and petitions were filed. The last two states to join the USA, Alaska and Hawaii, both sought the freedom and protection of being part of America. (Although there was considerable resistance by many Hawaiian natives.)

Another World War was a real possibility. In fact, it was more of a probability. Even the strongest of people trembled at the thought. Veterans were having nightmares again. Politicians were stressed to the point of failing health. Parents cried for their children's uncertain future. Nearly everyone hated and feared the "commies" in the Soviet Union. Yet here was communism in Cuba, just a few short miles off the coast of Florida. "Right in our own back yard," as Americans stated repeatedly.

The new president couldn't just ignore everyone's fears.

1961, April 17, The Bay of Pigs

Waves splashed over the sides of the overloaded boat. Because it was nighttime, the boat ride through and over the coral reefs was made even more harrowing. Even the bravest of the soldiers were unnerved. A cool breeze helped to relieve the heat generated from the heavy fatigues they were wearing, as they each carried three-quarters of their own weight in weapons and ammunition.

One Cuban rebel, a modest storeowner less than two years ago, turned to one of his comrades, a mere silhouette blocking a handful of stars, and asked his close friend and mentor, “José! Are we really going through with it this time?”

“Just remember our training, Chago, and be prepared for anything.” The rebel managed to pull off a commanding, confident tone despite the razor-sharp coral threatening the bottom of the boat. The owner of a shipping company in his former life, José was now a rebel with over two years of combat training under his belt.

He had been an outstanding business owner and a boss everyone admired in his previous life. He had always tried to lead by example and was not afraid to roll up his sleeves to help the workers on the docks, so it hadn’t taken long for him to bulk up from the intense training. Brains and brawn had earned José promotions, and before he knew it, he found himself in charge of training other rebels. “I’ve heard *Americanos* use the term,” José switched to English, “the third time’s a charm.”

The rebel boats headed for shore for the third night in a row. At this point, no one knew if they would begin the rebellion that night or if they would be called back to the ship, as they had been the previous two nights.

Other rebels within earshot took comfort in his words. They tended to draw much of their courage and drive from him. Many of his comrades had been business owners, teachers, or other degreed professionals in their former lives. Another man who had once been their hero had unsympathetically closed many of the businesses they owned or depended upon for their livelihood. Those businesses had been competing with the ones controlled by Fidel Castro. If the competitors for the companies he took over were cutting into his profits, the ruthless dictator simply closed them.

Now, the former business owners, engineers, and executives intended to overthrow the tyrant and take back their livelihoods. As his fellow revolutionists looked to José for confidence and leadership, he had looked to America and the American CIA agents he had come to know, even though very few were given permission to accompany them to the battle.

A Cuban rebel at the front of the boat began pointing frantically to a light that could only indicate that U.S. Special Forces operatives had made it to shore and were pointing the way to suitable landing positions. They all changed course slightly, but one of the boats failed to navigate completely around the coral and through a channel, as they impatiently veered directly toward the light.

Within seconds, the sounds of scraping and tearing metal were joined by the gurgling death screams of men as saltwater rushed into their lungs and open wounds. Waves tossed men back and forth over the coral, fraying their clothing as easily as their skin. Others went under without a struggle as the weight of their equipment pulled them down beneath the surface alongside the edge of the reef, drowning them without mercy or a fighting chance.

All the other boats continued to shore, under orders to advance at all costs. A wave tossed another landing craft onto the coral reef and those men suffered the same fate. The crew of three other boats, who were more aware of the situation, had slowed considerably, so when they hit the reef, they managed to back off to safety and remain where they were. The men in one of those boats used their hands to bail water continuously to prevent the craft from sinking.

Rebel boats moved in toward Bahía de Cochinos with about thirteen hundred troops. Some of the boats peeled off and landed on the beaches close to Playa Girón, and others went farther up the bay to Playa Larga. Several more boats had trouble navigating through the treacherous coral reefs, just as others had the previous two nights.

The Cubans who finally made it to shore, one battalion at Playa Girón and two at Playa Larga, yet again found no fellow rebels or "friendlies" there awaiting them. Nevertheless, the orders were to stay ashore this time.

Surprised rebels met resistance quickly. Too quickly. They were clearly expected and took heavy fire. By 3:00 a.m., Castro had been notified of the invasion and ordered nearly all his troops to move into place to fight the rebels. And that they did. Castro's army fought ferociously. They had to. The soldiers knew that if they did not, their families would be the ones to pay.

Bright sunlight from a spectacular sunrise soon suppressed the bursts of sparks and flames from the barrels of automatic weapons. The fighting raged on with few lulls. The two boats still offshore continued having problems getting through the coral and became easy targets for Castro's air support. The pilots spotted them in open water and effortlessly shot them full of holes. Survivors of the strafing were quickly torn to shreds by other means as the waves dragged them over the reef's jagged edges. Down with the boats went even more rebel ammunition and other supplies, such as fresh water and first aid.

Fierce fighting continued all morning and throughout the day as the rebels remained helplessly pinned down. "José! *José!* Where the hell are the *Americanos?*" Patience was already running thin, and anger began to build.

"I don't know, Chago! Perhaps they are busy destroying Castro's stronghold!" José had already determined that the CIA and America had abandoned them, but chose his words very carefully, saying only the things that might help keep his comrades alive long enough for someone to stage a rescue, or even a retreat.

Chago glanced up over the fallen palm tree they were hiding behind, squeezed off a shot at one of Castro's men, and ducked in time for a spray of projectiles to whiz over his head. The soldier he shot died within seconds, but not before wishing he hadn't tried to catch the attention of the owner of the store he had frequented on many occasions.

"José! I think I shot one of them!" Trying hard to sound excited, but failing, Chago was sick inside. Although he had fired many rounds in the general direction of his enemies, he had never actually seen a bullet hit its target. He had not had time to analyze his target's actions. He simply focused on the soldier's chest and squeezed the trigger. Thinking back, the man did not appear especially menacing; indeed, it looked as if the soldier had been looking straight at him, attempting to get his attention.

"Excellent! You are a good soldier, Chago. We will be victorious!" José rose, fired three quick rounds at random areas of the underbrush, and ducked again for cover. This caused another spray of lead into the palm in front of them and over their heads into the sand on the beach behind them.

"José!"

"Yes, my friend?"

"Are we going to try to make those mountains tonight?"

Mountains? The CIA agents who had trained them had suggested several contingency plans for situations such as the one where they now found themselves.

One such plan was to flee to the safety of nearby mountains. There appeared to be some large hills some distance away, on the other side of what looked like several miles of mud and swamps, but even if they were able to get through the swamps, the distant hills did not offer much in the way of cover. Quite the opposite, in fact. It mattered little, however, as they were pinned down, and there didn't seem to be a way for any of them to make it off the beach. The "mountains" were not an option.

Chago took the silence of his mentor to mean that they would *not* be trying to make it to the mountains.

When they dove for cover the night before, they had been forced to break up into small groups, but they still managed to get messages around to most of their troops. By late afternoon their numbers had dwindled to fewer than twelve hundred rebels, and some twenty thousand Cuban soldiers surrounded them. Despite still being able to communicate, none of the rebels had any way of knowing that President Kennedy had ordered the CIA and all air support to stand down and for U.S. ships to move even farther from Cuba, as if to distance himself from the failed overthrow efforts.

Facing the beach, many of Castro's soldiers fired over the rebels' heads, wasting ammo purposely, hoping that somehow their brothers would find a way to fight through the overwhelming odds. Many Castro loyalists secretly wished they could have joined such a cause and been heroes to the people. Other soldiers, however, tried desperately to kill the rebels and did not dare risk showing any sign of support for these brave men. They had seen firsthand what Castro's elitists could do to a man's wife and children.

Intense fighting continued for two full days. Each rebel had left the transport ship with a full canteen of water, but José had not had a sip in over forty-eight hours because he had thrown his canteen to two wounded comrades behind a low-lying dune. Chago had offered José a drink of his water, but he had refused, and even though his canteen was full, Chago refused to drink as long as José was doing without. They waited—and endured.

Finally, Kennedy ordered air support to go in to try to save at least some of the rebels, but, adding insult to injury, four American pilots were shot down and killed instead. Out of ammunition and patience, the rebel communications officer radioed in, cursed the people on the receiving end, and then they all made a run for the swamps.

Nearly twelve hundred exhausted rebels were taken prisoner, including the two former business owners who had been side-by-side since they first embarked on those small boats over forty-eight hours earlier. They had helped each other stay alive by watching each other's backs and were now as close as brothers. Over a hundred rebels in the invasion force were killed on the beaches during the fighting or in the boats while trying to get ashore.

"José! José!" Chago tried to ask his friend a question without drawing their captors' attention. He saw José looking at him through the corner of one eye without turning his head. "What will they do with us? What will become of us now?"

It was difficult to remain stoic while experiencing the humility of being shackled to hundreds of your fellow revolutionaries and facing charges of treason. He had mistakenly trusted the *Americanos* and followed them to this disaster. Chago and many others had, in turn, followed *him* into battle, and he had let them down the same way the new American president had disappointed this band of revolutionists. A slow, seething anger began to boil within him.

From José's lack of response, Chago knew this wouldn't end well for them. He felt as if he did not fight hard enough. Overcome with shame, he was overwhelmed with thoughts of being inadequate and dishonorable.

Most Americans were ashamed of their country's actions, and some wondered what kind of mess they had gotten into by electing such a young president.

The press and international communities had a field day with the failure of the Kennedy administration, but he publicly took personal responsibility for the failure, and the American public soon forgave him. JFK was not so forgiving of Dulles and Secretary of State Dean Rusk, who should have kept him better informed and offered other options.

Kennedy decided to rein in the CIA and began drafting a bill intended to ensure that future presidents would have complete control over the CIA. Jack should have kept the bill confidential and found someone to represent it to Congress. Instead, he formed a public committee to determine how best to change the CIA so that power and decisions flowed through the White House. He even assigned Dulles, the head of the CIA, to the committee.

Under his stoic mask, Dulles bristled at the thought of losing control of the CIA. He believed that he and his agency were the only obstacles between communism and the American way of life. Being on the committee assigned to undermine his own efforts to protect America made Dulles develop even more contempt and hatred for the young, spoiled Kennedy brothers.

1961, April–May, Atlanta, Georgia

David Ferrie looked a bit disheveled as he plopped down into the pilot's seat with a heavy sigh, his copilot looking at him in disbelief.

"Aw, hell! You look like shit. Didn't anyone ever tell you you're supposed to *relax* while you're on vacation?"

Ferrie knew better than to get into details, but making his copilot wonder sounded like fun. "Yeah, well, looking back, relaxing might have been a much better option for *everyone*."

The copilot knew better than to nibble at Ferrie's bait but, before he could stop himself, he asked, "Huh?"

"Nothing! Forget it. Let's just get this bird checked out. When we get in the air, I'm going to need you to take the stick for a while."

"Aye, aye, sir."

A few short weeks later, Ferrie was in a much smaller, two-prop plane, fighting the heavy winds of a torrential rainstorm. He was trying to land the craft on a small, privately owned runway a few miles outside New Orleans that was unlit except for runway marker lights.

Under normal conditions, a copilot would be helping him in a plane this size, and he *wished* he had some help, too. In these adverse conditions, he *should* have had some help. For this trip, though, the individual who ordered the flight insisted that he fly solo to Guatemala and then New Orleans.

Heavy winds whipped the tail of the craft around as though it were a windsock, and sheets of rain pounded the windshield with a frightful force. The two passengers in the back of the plane yelled out occasionally, demanding yet another update on the situation. Ferrie answered in a voice meant to convey confidence, but they could tell he was as concerned as they were.

Turbulence shook the aircraft violently enough to make them believe the wind would shear the wings off the fuselage. Both passengers gripped their armrests tightly enough to cause their fingers and knuckles to turn a shade of white, approaching that of their ashen faces. One had his eyes open wide, and the other had his shut tightly.

Because all the lights in and on the aircraft were out to reduce the chances of anyone seeing the plane land, neither man could see the other's reaction to the severe storm. The darkness and the occasional lightning flashes, close enough to blind them both temporarily, added an additional fear factor to the ride.

Finally, the runway marker lights appeared through the rain as the plane descended through low-lying clouds. Ferrie immediately noticed that he was off center by a fraction too much, so he made a split-second decision to make a correction. At that precise moment, a gust of wind pushed the craft in the same direction, causing his action to be an overcorrection. This caused even more alarm and stress in his passengers, but both were too frightened to demand another report from their pilot.

Another split-second decision had Ferrie adjusting his overcorrection. Simultaneously, he had to correct their descent so that he would be flying straight and level when the wheels contacted the runway. Ferrie wished he could turn on the plane's landing lights so that he could at least see the darkened runway. Instinct let him know he was descending too fast, so he adjusted again, and just in time. The wheels hit the ground harder and farther down the runway than he would have liked, but the landing was acceptable, considering the circumstances.

Mentally patting himself on the back and congratulating himself on his superior piloting skills, Ferrie nearly laughed aloud with relief. His passengers, on the other hand, had a different viewpoint. They did not praise him for his fine piloting skills or for landing the plane safely in such a fierce storm. At night. Using only sketchy, storm-distorted radar and the runway marker lights. Instead, they cursed him and insulted him.

Worst of all, they told him that *he* owed *them* huge favors because of the rough, horrible flight. *Huge* favors. It didn't matter that he had put his life and job on hold for two days and had risked his very life to *illegally* fly his two passengers out of a bad situation during a raging storm to help cover their entrance back into the United States.

The last thing anyone needed was to be indebted to Carlos Marcello and one of his "attorneys." He thought the two men would be grateful after all they had been through in Central America.

1961, June 3 & 4, Vienna

John F. Kennedy met with Soviet Premier Nikita Khrushchev to discuss critical international issues, such as disarmament, a divisive East German treaty the Soviets were threatening to sign, the political disputes in Laos, and nuclear testing. Kennedy was failing miserably to persuade Khrushchev to agree with any of his global-centric positions, and the aging Soviet premier was becoming angrier and angrier with the younger, well-educated Kennedy.

Khrushchev began lecturing Kennedy about successful leadership techniques throughout recent world history, but JFK's knowledge of history was extensive and truly impressive. He was able to counter every point Khrushchev made with fresher, more modern views. As they parted ways, the diehard communist knew the American was correct, and that infuriated him.

Still, they issued a joint public statement that promised to "maintain contact on all questions of interest to the two countries and for the whole world."

Boldly lying where many have lied before, Khrushchev eagerly reported to the people of the Soviet Union how Kennedy had threatened war between the two superpowers. Instead of acknowledging the wisdom of the younger world leader, and working toward peaceful coexistence, Khrushchev spurred even more Soviet hatred and fear, which significantly increased the collective paranoia in the East, and ultimately led to the building of the wall between East and West Berlin. Instead of rekindling the friendships between hemispheres, as Kennedy intended to do, Khrushchev unnecessarily taught his comrades to hate Kennedy and all Americans.

Kennedy was aware of the purpose of Khrushchev's bullying. He and the United States had been seriously threatened and challenged to a fight. Kennedy also realized that the lies and twisted truths Khrushchev was spewing to the world were typical of a bully who tries to draw a crowd to watch a fight.

Kennedy and Khrushchev *did* meet again. By proxy, in Southeast Asia, almost entirely in Vietnam. While the entire world watched, the superpowers fought in someone else's back yard. Despite the anticipation of Khrushchev's onlookers, the governments used the term "Police Action" to describe one of the most brutal and important wars in planet Earth's history.

Labeling the conflict in Vietnam a police action freed all those involved from officially declaring war on each other and averted many of the needs and responsibilities associated with answering to voters and other branches of government. The governments of two powerful countries fought a war in the jungles of a weakened country far away from their own precious cities, and got away with it.

Only the leaders of governments could be held responsible, but nearly all the ones who would hold them responsible agreed with their tactics of offsite scrimmages. There was virtually no accountability. Even newspapers and the news media were stifled, either by choice or by fear of retaliation.

The suffering in Vietnam was appalling. Not just humans suffered, but also animals and plant life. It was truly a "scorch the earth" situation. A tactical chemical called Agent Orange killed vast tracts of jungle, and millions of wildlife inhabitants died as a result. For *decades* to follow, people and animals exposed to the defoliator, or even the wilted jungle after the fact, became sick and died of a barrage of complications.

This clash between governments with conflicting views resulted in an unbridled and widespread hatred of John F. Kennedy. Hundreds of thousands of people who were unfortunate enough to be adversely affected by the conflict in Vietnam wanted Kennedy and Khrushchev dead. Most people blamed both leaders for the conflict but, out of fear, only voiced their criticisms of the United States and the U.S. president. Few understood that the superpowers were deeply embroiled in what would have been World War III had all the battles not been waged on a single battlefield.

JFK and his administration could have, and probably *should* have, initiated an informative campaign to educate Americans so they would understand that the war was going to be fought somewhere, and *any*where was better than fighting it in the cities of the United States. Of course, Soviet leaders felt the same way about their own cities, as did the Vietnamese, who were forced to make unspeakable sacrifices for uncaring foreigners.

The information campaign could have also included other life lessons, such as how far too many people vent their frustrations with situations that are out of their control by supporting the position they fear most. They throw their support behind those they fear, usually a bully. Never mind the fact that this behavior is often detrimental to their own well-being.

Many people feel a rush of power when they side with those they fear. It's also a relatively easy trap to fall into because people often have feelings of power or even protection when they associate themselves with those they fear or see as powerful. It can be quite intoxicating if they can align themselves with those they see as more powerful than those who have authority over their lives. It's a common defense mechanism, although not a very healthy one.

The longer the conflict continued, the more people learned to hate the young president they elected.

1961, August 26, Miami, Florida

Eddie Rickenbacker argued with an Eastern Air Lines HR employee on the other end of his telephone line. He couldn't make him understand that they simply could not keep an employee like Ferrie employed after *two arrests*, especially if there was any truth to the charges of improper behavior with minor boys.

The director of HR made his case to retain Ferrie quite eloquently, as only a master manipulator could. His position was to keep Ferrie until they found a replacement because being short one pilot could mean that ticketing would be unable to overbook passengers for a while, and some passengers might even get bumped to a later flight. The director gently reminded Rickenbacker that many Eastern Air Lines passengers were loyal because they knew that if their flights became too full, another plane would roll out within minutes, allowing them to fly on a far less crowded plane.

Rickenbacker insisted that Eastern Air Lines wouldn't have any passengers *at all* if the press decided to put the worst possible spin on the story. He knew that a bad image planted by a popular reporter could hurt business for *years*.

"Take Ferrie off the payroll, now." A short pause. "No, now. I'll wait here on the phone with you while your people handle the paperwork. You can give me the blow-by-blow as you do the paperwork." Another short pause. "I *am* a very busy man. I *do* have many other things I could be doing, but none of those things are nearly as important as this." A long pause. "Yes, I'm still here, are you finished yet? How about now? Now? Are they finished now? Yeah? Walk a copy of that up to me, right now. Thank you! I'll see you in five or ten minutes, right? Goodbye."

Eddie Rickenbacker didn't compete in the Indianapolis 500 four times, shoot down twenty-six German airplanes during WWI, earn the Medal of Honor, operate an entire airline, or survive *two* plane crashes and twenty-four days in a raft near Japanese-held territory by being passive. He was not about to be manipulated by an HR personnel director.

Rickenbacker's efforts infuriated Ferrie so much that he publicly criticized Rickenbacker on several occasions. The vindictive pilot bragged to anyone who would listen that he was a *far* superior pilot than the World War I hero. Ferrie also retained the services of a New Orleans attorney named G. Wray Gill to take legal action against Eastern Air Lines.

Gill just *happened* to be the very same attorney that Carlos Marcello was using to represent him in his deportation hearing, so to help pay for Gill's services, Ferrie agreed to serve as a part-time pilot and "errand boy" when Gill had urgent business in other cities or, more likely, in Central America. Ferrie would also work with William Guy Banister, a former FBI agent, as private investigators on the Marcello case.

Ferrie often met with Banister at his office in the Newman Building, at the corner of Lafayette Avenue and Camp Street in New Orleans.

1961, September, The Oval Office

Kennedy sat at his desk dictating a letter into his Dictaphone. The recipients of the correspondence were the CEOs of America's twelve largest steel companies and the steelworkers' union. In as reasonable a tone as oral dictation that was intended for written correspondence would allow, he urged them to act responsibly during the negotiations for an upcoming labor contract.

He intended to make sure both parties understood that the sudden increases of salaries for large numbers of people inevitably increased prices. This would likely trigger other increases which would result in a chain reaction and cause a spike in inflation. In the letter, he requested that the steel industry not raise prices again after a scheduled price increase the following month.

Playing the letter back to himself, he found that his words sounded futile.

During the recording, a three-year-old girl ran into the room saying, "Daddy, I drew you a flower!" Kennedy took a piece of paper from his daughter's outstretched hand and admired the swirls of multicolored scribbles, assuring her that it was quite beautiful and insisting it must be a rare orchid. Throughout this exchange, the Dictaphone was still recording.

Caroline Bouvier Kennedy laughed her wonderful laugh and simply said, "Yeah!" She ran back down the hall, very likely wondering about rare orchids, just as her daddy had hoped.

Days later, contrasting sharply with his daughter's sweet innocence and delight, the reaction JFK received from his letter from both sides of the steel industry's labor negotiations was antagonistic, at best. Press releases blasted their respective opponents—and the president. Tossing his newspaper aside, Kennedy remarked to his brother that the CEOs of the steel industry *and* the union leaders could easily be some of America's most greedy and self-centered people.

Jack and Bobby also understood that the strongly negative words in the press statements were likely toned down before going to print. They both understood that such contempt often sprouted from the deep-rooted resentment and jealousy that many hard-working people had toward those they considered privileged.

1961, November, The Jungles of Vietnam

An old Vietnamese man squatted in thick foliage with his left knee on the ground. The wrist of his right arm rested on his right knee while his hand dangled most of the time but occasionally tensed up. His left hand slowly stroked the long, gray whiskers around his mouth, a habit for decades. Lost in thought, he recalled the speech given by Ho Chi Minh years earlier in which he quoted some of America's Declaration of Independence.

That speech had given him and his countrymen courage; however, the hope of Western help and support had long since eroded into bitter hatred for the United States and its capitalistic ways.

Weary from the long, disappointing past that had at first held so much promise, the old soldier's thoughts continued to drift back through the years. Long before Ho Chi Minh made that speech in 1945, the old soldier had fought the Japanese. Before that, he had fought the French for years, as his father and grandfather had done, as well.

This war was different, though. For the first time, he was fighting his own countrymen. It didn't make any difference to him, though. He no longer had compassion for any living thing, except that of his immediate family. His Vietnamese brothers in the south were as much his enemy as the Americans. He had fought and killed them because his leader told him he had to do that. A good soldier. He attributed his long life to the fact that he had always been a good soldier.

Without bothering to look, he reached down to brush ants off his foot and shifted his stiff legs into the alternate position. Now, his right knee was on the ground, and his left wrist was resting on his knee. He was closely watching the northeast trail, which led into a small coastal village just outside the city of Phuong Cát Son.

The old soldier had been warned repeatedly that the Americans were coming and that they were the most formidable enemies his people had ever faced. Yet he was confident that the "Yankees" would be driven from Vietnam. All the invaders, for as long as he, his father, and his grandfather before him could remember, had been defeated and expelled from his homeland.

He had recently been told that Americans were trying to rush in to take over and govern them in their evil, capitalist ways. He would fight to the death to prevent the ruthless American warriors from eating his grandchildren and taking all the women in his village.

Long before anyone came into view, the old man could hear his Viet Cong comrades approaching. This time, however, he heard and smelled something different about them. Only when he knew they were close enough to be seen through the dense jungle did he turn. His comrades, smartly dressed in Soviet-style jungle garb, were sporting new Soviet weapons. Powerful-looking weapons, unlike any he had ever seen.

Without a word, he knew it was time. After leading them through the jungle, off the well-worn path and from a direction rarely used, they waited near the edge of the village until he heard a voice he couldn't understand coming from a strange, unfamiliar black box. He did, however, know what the nod from the Soviet commander meant and led his comrades into the village. They forced the frightened villagers out of their homes and into the center of the community. They searched the contents of huts and dug through stores of rice.

"At least *we* won't eat their children," the old man thought as he watched two Viet Cong soldiers shoot several unarmed, harmless people and then begin to burn anything that they might later claim looked suspicious. He heard children crying hysterically and women screaming in pain and anguish as lines of soldiers raped them repeatedly. Yet he showed no emotion.

"At least *we* will leave the women alive when we are finished with them."

His leaders had taught him that when people embrace capitalism, and therefore the enemy, this was the price they paid. However, the old soldier did not take personal pleasures with any of the South Vietnamese women, for a good soldier did not participate in such behavior. Neither did he try to help any of them, though, for he understood that this was punishment for their treason.

These conflicting concepts reeled in his mind as he tried to resolve them into military rules and regulations. He didn't think that soldiers should benefit from the punishment of others. When he could not disentangle the conflict in his mind, he blamed the Americans for causing it all.

Nearly eighty-six hundred miles away, in Washington, DC, President John F. Kennedy struggled with his own dilemma. He knew that if he didn't send more U.S. "advisors" into South Vietnam, the people there would not stand a chance of ever enjoying any kind of democracy or having free elections.

If he pulled the existing advisors out, communism would surge into the void left by American efforts to spark democracy in the region. Kennedy also knew that if he sent in more troops and aid, so too would China and the Soviets, armed with Khrushchev's state-of-the-art weapons.

Despite the sickening feeling in his gut, he sighed heavily and picked up the phone. Leaning all the way back in his chair, just as Eisenhower had done so many times before him, he ordered more *advisors* into Vietnam.

1962, January 30, Minsk, USSR

Lee Harvey Oswald was very upset, despite the American Embassy's spectacular view of the city and the lush forests in the north. The rolling hills in the northeast and rivers flowing into Lukomskaye Lake in the northwest were also a remarkable sight. Yet, to him, the beauty of the city and the surrounding Minsk Province had been recently diminished, along with his perception of communism and the Soviet way of life.

His disenchantment with communism began when he did not receive the kind of welcome he assumed he would get, one he felt he deserved. After all, he had abandoned his American way of life to embrace *their* way of life, yet no one considered him a hero, and he could tell that, secretly, some of them thought he was an idiot for leaving America. He also knew why no one in the Soviet Union wanted to voice this opinion.

Marguerite Oswald was explaining the letter she had sent to her son in which she stated that the Marines had issued him a dishonorable discharge. Lee had to press the phone against his ear to hear her through the static and noise, but he clearly heard her repeat "dishonorable discharge" and not "undesirable discharge," which he believed was the case.

His mother also insisted repeatedly that she knew the Soviets were holding him there against his will and that she genuinely believed that he was a patriot, an honorable soldier, and a good American. When he had heard enough, he hung up on her, gave himself a moment to allow the anger to subside, and began pressing the embassy staff to do everything in their power to see to it that the U.S. government granted him a speedy exit from the Soviet Union.

While still in the American Embassy, Oswald wrote a letter to John Bowden Connally Jr., whom he considered a "fellow Texan" even though Oswald was from New Orleans, but more importantly, whom he believed was still the secretary of the Navy. Thinking that Connally might use his considerable influence over the board that oversaw unfavorable discharges, Oswald asked Connally to reverse the decision and change his discharge status to something more favorable.

Connally didn't know what to think of the letter since it came from red Russia and since it requested him to overturn a decision on a dishonorable discharge that was not "dishonorable." The new governor of Texas correctly assumed that any answer he personally provided would not be enough to satisfy Oswald. Still, as a courtesy to a fellow veteran, he forwarded the letter to the Marines.

1962, September 12, Rice University

JFK stood behind a podium delivering what would become one of his most famous speeches. Though he was sweating liberally and was miserable in the stifling Houston heat and humidity, he managed to turn the situation around to his advantage by joking about the heat and his discomfort. The Texans loved him, however, his "Race to the Moon" proposal wasn't accepted by everyone else quite as readily as many of his other ideas.

Kennedy's financial commitment to the new space program angered many who believed that all that money would be better spent on social programs and creating new jobs (in some other states not already rich in oil).

Nearly every member of the United Nations was incensed to the point of being offended by the notion of "racing" to the moon. They could not believe Kennedy wouldn't use this opportunity to promote world peace. They all agreed that a joint mission to the moon should be a cooperative global affair rather than a competition with the winner already known well in advance.

Many people in and around JFK's home in the Northeast were angry and felt betrayed as Kennedy, one of their own, announced that most of the new major space program operations would be established in the South and on the West Coast. Texas, Florida, and California would enjoy the majority of the financial benefits of the innovative, cutting-edge space program. Taxpayers throughout the Northeast believed their taxes would migrate south with the birds and waste away down there.

Even after a hundred years, the Civil War still raged in the minds of many people.

1962, October 16–28, Cuba

Eisenhower had sanctioned an escalating trade embargo against Cuba, but it had little to no impact on the dictatorship. One of his last acts as president had been to officially cut off diplomatic relations between Cuba and the United States. The timing of this action has always been a little suspect. Did Eisenhower sever the diplomatic ties to make it easier for the next president? Or did he do it so the young Kennedy wouldn't have the chance to show him up by resolving long-standing issues with Castro?

Either way, Kennedy certainly stepped into a hot zone when he took office, as he found out when he allowed the Eisenhower-initiated, CIA-led Cuban invasion to continue. The circumstances surrounding Cuba and the Soviets had done nothing but worsen over the past year and a half. The dramatic scene ninety miles off the Florida coast had gradually deteriorated, slowly unraveling out of control. At the forefront of the chaos was America's refusal to continue to buy tons of Cuban sugar. As a result, Cuba made a painfully obvious but sweet deal with the Soviet Union to trade all that sugar for arms and military equipment.

Whenever the U.S. pulled out of diplomatic relations with another country, others, like the Soviet Union, interjected theirs, whether the receiving party liked it or not. Fear kept Castro in line with Soviet "requests," just as Castro used fear to control his fellow Cubans.

Against his better judgment, Fidel Castro agreed to allow Khrushchev to set up nuclear missiles in his country so that the Soviets would have an answer to U.S. nukes in Turkey. It was a simple matter of equalizing strategy in the eyes of those involved, as though they had no concept of the horrific possibilities.

The young, inexperienced president made monumental diplomatic efforts to keep the peace, but they were insufficient. Diplomatic efforts were met with more Soviet belligerence. Everyone knew the reason for the Soviets' aggressiveness was the presence of U.S. nuclear missiles in Turkey, pointing straight at Moscow. Most of the civilized world knew that the only way to rid Cuba of Russian nukes was to pull the American missiles out of Turkey. Anyone who knew anything about people understood that a military strike to render the nuclear launching sites in Cuba inoperable would result in a similar Soviet strike in Turkey. Balance.

Kennedy and his administration had multiple possibilities open to them, but ultimately, they chose a path that allowed both countries to save face. A show of military force would appear to force the Soviet Union to back off Cuba, and, in return, the United States would quietly remove their missiles from Turkey over the following few months.

Most people with the qualities to drive them to be president of the United States would not have had the patience or the nerves to tolerate the presence of nuclear arms in Cuba. Most people in Kennedy's position would have likely ordered an air strike on Cuba immediately and then retaliated against the Soviet Union for striking American friends in Turkey, all the while blaming the communists. Kennedy walked a thin political tightrope over a precarious abyss, balancing the entire world on his shoulders.

For this act alone, Kennedy deserved the status of Twentieth-Century Superhero. He saved us all. Nearly every man, woman, child, animal, and plant owe their existence to John F. Kennedy. Yet the decisions Kennedy made that ultimately saved us all still angered the people who did not have all the facts. Some of them didn't even want to know the facts. They just wanted to hate.

Many military men saw the pullout of nuclear arms from Turkey as weak leadership and chose to loathe their commander-in-chief for it. Some of them openly showed contempt and disrespect. More than just a few of those men were willing to do *anything* to protect their vision of the American way of life. And some of *those* men had the knowledge and means to eliminate anyone they felt threatened their way of life.

Across the Atlantic, Turkey had reluctantly agreed to accept the nukes into their country, which was a significant investment, so the United States government would offer them protection from communist expansion. Several trusted Turkish political leaders made profound personal sacrifices so that America could slip nuclear missiles into their country. With the Americans seemingly pulling out of Turkey altogether, the future looked quite bleak for the average Turk. Many felt betrayed or abandoned and passionately despised Kennedy for this.

Presidents often spend a good deal of time and resources cleaning up the previous administrations' chaos. Kennedy was no exception. Not only did he have to clean up messes, he left a few of his own. The nuclear missiles the Eisenhower administration placed in Turkey were old, obsolete weapons that may not have been in working order. No one knew what would have happened had someone tried to fire the weapons, and even less was known about what would have happened had the Soviets dealt an air strike.

1963, January, Michigan

(Exact locations and dates are lost to history.)

A topless waitress with one of the best artificial smiles anyone had ever produced placed open bottles of beer on the table in a darkened corner of a nightclub not yet open for the day. James "Jimmy" Riddle Hoffa handed the server a bill too large for her to make change and swatted her on the behind as she walked away. She was so used to it, though, she barely noticed.

"Keep da change, honey." What did he care? He wasn't spending *his* money.

The men at the table watched the flowing, bouncing movements of her luscious cheeks as she walked away, enjoying the obvious show she'd adopted in an attempt to increase her tips.

"Mm, mm, mmm," Jimmy uttered before snapping out of it, but then got right down to business with a somewhat quieter statement that should have come as a shock to the other men, but didn't. "Get with Santos and Carlos. Tell 'em I want Kennedy outta da picture. For good."

After a few moments of silence, Hoffa's attorney, Frank Ragano, asks, "How the hell they supposta do that?"

"What am I, a hit man now? I don't know! That's why I want da boys to do it. If anyone could pull dat off, it's those two goons."

Nods and expressions of agreement formed a consensus.

1963, February 17, The Oval Office

John F. Kennedy sighed and rubbed his eyes. He called out to the lead Secret Service agent on the other side of the door, which swung open immediately.

"Sir?"

"Bobby and I have been at this for hours. Can we get Jill and Priscilla back to the White House?"

Hiding his disgust at having to supply his boss with prostitutes once again, he dropped a noticeable, but deserved, hint. "Sir, I don't know if Fiddle and Faddle will be available this late on a Sunday evening."

"Well, do your best," retorted JFK. "And, we have too much to do tonight to leave the Oval Office, so just escort them in he-ah. I'll just bend mine over my desk."

The brothers laughed, but the Secret Service agent looked at the classified documents scattered all over the president's desktop.

Jacqueline "Jackie" Lee Bouvier Kennedy Onassis, Jacqueline Kennedy at the time, was an elegant woman about as perfect a First Lady as one could ask for. However, she was publicly and privately humiliated countless times by JFK, who was a compulsive womanizer. Besides the prostitutes, there were also models, actresses, and international spies who often shared a bed with JFK. Although prostitutes were usually hired in pairs. One for his brother Bobby, too. The two of them had a stream of women entertaining them on a regular basis.

Jackie always appeared calm, cool, and collected, but on the inside, she was simmering with anger. Very few times did Jackie let that anger surface, but she was once giving a tour of the White House to a French reporter and happened across Priscilla "Fiddle" Wear, either by chance or by design, no one knows for sure. She told the reporter that Priscilla was one of the girls "who is supposedly sleeping with my husband." Jackie was aware of JFK's womanizing.

More than a couple of Secret Service agents were seething with anger as well, after having the careers they worked so hard to obtain be reduced to providing prostitutes for immoral men. Instead of guarding the president from assassins, or from terrorist organizations intent on taking him hostage, they were there to simply prevent Jackie from entering until they could escort the girls out another door.

Each time a prostitute came in contact with Kennedy, the anger in several men, and at least one woman, increased exponentially.

1963, March 31, Dallas

Lee Harvey Oswald strapped his holster around his waist, shoved his new .38 caliber Smith & Wesson revolver into it, and admired himself in a mirror. Black slacks, black shirt, and a pistol on his hip like a gunslinger from the old Wild West.

He liked what he saw, so he readied the only camera he had available that contained film. His plastic Imperial 620 Duo Lens. The camera was so cheap it even had plastic lenses. He ordered his wife outside into the back yard, as though they were militants, as he picked up his other new firearm, an old, bolt-action Italian military surplus Carcano Model 38 from WWII. He had recently mail-ordered the rifle and the pistol using a post office box and "A. Hidell" as an alias.

As an afterthought to what was already quite the spontaneous act, Oswald picked up two Russian newspapers on the way out of the back door. If he were going to take pictures of this nature, he might as well display his lingering preference for communism as well.

Ironically, Oswald would have remembered that he would not have been able to own those guns in the USSR.

As his Russian wife, Marina, fumbled with the camera, he shifted into several poses holding the newspapers up and brandishing his rifle. A very uncomfortable Marina worried about the neighbors witnessing the spectacle. The rest of the Sunday was not much better for either of them.

With the honeymoon obviously in the past, the Oswalds went to bed angry after a full weekend of badgering and pointless bickering over too many trivial matters. Lee woke up with the Monday morning blues, and when he arrived at his job at Jaggars-Chiles-Stovall, a printing and typography company, his manager presented him with a one-week notice.

Oswald was told he was being terminated for inefficiency, imprecision, and for the argumentative attitude he maintained with his coworkers, particularly when the discussion turned to politics, which was far too often.

He told himself that losing the job did not matter, as he already had everything he needed from the company. While working alone in the building during weekends and the occasional late evening, he had used their professional printing and photographic equipment to create false identification under the name Alek J. Hidell. He had also been in the "secured" areas and had seen all the new maps of Cuba the company was printing for the Department of Defense, which piqued his curiosity. If the DoD still had an interest in Cuba, then maybe he should be interested as well.

Still, the loss of any job bothered him. Despite his best efforts, his entire life had been one disappointment after another, and people constantly rated him and his performance as below average. One of the only times in his life that he performed above average was his rating as a Sharpshooter in the United States Marines, which did little for him in the job market, and the fact that he had left the Marines with an "Undesirable Discharge" meant that he could never return to the military.

1963, April 10, Dallas

Even more sullen than usual, Lee Harvey Oswald pushed his unfinished dinner plate away. While Marina did the dishes, he wandered into their tiny bedroom, placed a note on their bed in the event that he didn't return, then left the apartment without a word. He walked a block to a parking lot at the corner of North Zang Boulevard, where East Davis Street turns into West Davis Street, to meet a man he barely knew.

As Oswald climbed into the passenger seat, he sneaked a peek into the back seat and saw his own Carcano rifle half covered with what looked like a Weatherman jacket. The driver started the engine immediately but drove away slowly. Another car at the curb switched on its headlights and pulled in behind them. When the lights illuminated the inside of their car, Oswald snapped his head around quickly and looked into the lights with a wide-eyed, nervous look on his face.

After a short twenty-minute trip, the driver of the car behind them peeled off and disappeared up an alley. Oswald's ride pulled into a church parking lot and parked amongst the other cars owned by those attending a Wednesday night service. The driver reached up and removed the dome light from its socket. Then they both sat quietly for a moment, looking around.

Seeing no one, Oswald reached into the back seat and retrieved his rifle. He pulled the bolt back to confirm there was indeed a cartridge in the chamber. Satisfied, he stepped out of the car and quietly pushed the door closed. Oswald snaked his way between several cars to the house next door to the church.

Trying to gain the best vantage point, he moved around from one place to another, comparing different angles and looking in every window where even the dimmest of light shone. When the occasional car passed by, he threw himself to the ground or crouched behind a bush or tree trunk, holding himself perfectly still. Despite his best efforts, however, he could not make his target who, unseen and silent, was somewhere inside the house. He made his way back to the car.

“You didn’t take the shot? What the hell?”

“I cannot locate the target within the house.”

“How do you expect to advance if you have no patience at all?”

“He’s already gone to bed!”

“The lights are still on!” Gawking at the house, he added, “The lights are on downstairs and none have come on upstairs. He has NOT gone to bed.”

Oswald looked over, clearly able to see the lights were indeed still on, but he said nothing.

“If we drive away from here before you take your shot, it is *over*. You will not be trusted again.”

Shaking his head at his own mediocrity, he creeped out of the car again, made his way back to their target, and placed himself in a position beside a tree. From this vantage point, he was almost entirely concealed from passing cars, and he was able to peer into a window where he had seen his target sit at a desk each night he had watched the house in the past.

The driver of the car that had followed them stepped out of his sedan and, walking over to the car Oswald had been in, asked the driver, “The scope is still in its manufactured position, right? No shims? No chance of being accurate?”

“Yes, of course. I told you I had this under control.”

The flickering light from a Zippo lighter lit up the face of the man standing by the car. He said nothing, but sucked in a long drag of choking comfort, the tip of the cigarette glowing bright enough to momentarily cast his face in dim orange light.

Most people are creatures of habit, and on that night, this axiom proved to be true. Briskly walking into his office to sit at his desk, in plain view of the wannabe assassin outside his window, was Edwin A. Walker. The very man who had overseen the integration of Little Rock High School after the Supreme Court ruling on Brown v. Board of Education. Walker had also been relieved of command, and publicly admonished by the Kennedy administration, for distributing literature printed by the ultraconservative John Birch Society.

Taking careful aim at Walker's chest, Oswald squeezed the trigger. Without waiting to see the results of his actions, he dashed back to the car. The other vehicle that had followed them there was already speeding down the alley, fleeing the scene by the time Lee reached the church parking lot. The driver of his car already had the engine running and the passenger door open for him, so Oswald jumped in and stashed the rifle on the back floorboard. They sped out of the parking lot before he could close his door. Moments later, they made their one and only scheduled stop so Oswald could stash his rifle.

While the car sped south on I-35E, only one thing broke the silence. "You've proven your worth and *will* be contacted about another important operation in the near future. Will you be ready?"

Lee nodded, but he was pale and unable to speak. He tried to appear masculine yet uncaring about taking another human's life. In truth, he was nauseous and wishing one of his suicide attempts had been successful.

He rocked to the motion created by the uneven roads, staring at the striped white lines on the interstate. He did not remember the driver dropping him off a block from his home, but eventually he realized that he was sitting in the front yard of his rented apartment. When he went inside, he found Marina distraught, wondering what was wrong. She had already found the note he left earlier, which now seemed like a lifetime ago, even though it had only been a couple of hours. Marina pestered him until she found out what he had done.

Morning brought a new light for Oswald. The radio cheerfully reported that “Ted” Walker was alive and well, with minor injuries to his arm after a failed assassination attempt. Oswald was both relieved and angered. “How could I have missed from less than a hundred feet?” He told Marina that he wished he had killed the man the same way he wished someone had killed Hitler before he raped the world. However, he made no more attempts to kill Walker, and he burned most of his plans and reconnaissance photos in their bathtub.

When no one came to arrest him, Oswald was pleased, if not emboldened, feeling as if he had a new lease on life. When he arose the next morning, a Friday, he shaved, put on a white shirt and tie, and went downtown to file for unemployment.

1963, Early May, New Orleans

David Ferrie asked Clay Shaw to find Oswald a job so they could keep him close. Shaw refused to use his considerable influence to help Oswald at first, until Ferrie explained.

"Now w*hy* would I do *anything* to help a *known* commie and Castro supporter who's trying to infiltrate our ranks for—*who knows* what?"

"Think it through, man! We can use this gullible, idealistic stooge to our advantage. If we play our cards right, we can get him to do anything we want."

"You think so?" Shaw was already becoming sexually aroused by Ferrie's passion, which was something they both counted on when they had the opportunity to be alone together.

"Yes, of course. I've used him before, and like I said, he's as gullible as a child. We'll have him out there in no time, passing out pamphlets that defend Castro and communism. He will look like a kook, and we will be able to pin *anything* on him. We can't overthrow Castro all by ourselves. If the president of the United States couldn't do it, we'll need all the help we can get. Especially the unwitting, disposable kind of help." Ferrie recognized Shaw's arousal and did his best to excite the man further.

"Well, I don't know, but perhaps there *is* something you can do to convince me to help this poor man..."

1963, May 9, New Orleans

About a block and a half from the Newman Building, where David Ferrie and Clay Shaw often met with William "Bill" B. Reily, Oswald began his employment at the Reily Coffee Co. Reily, the owner, was a major contributor to several anti-Castro organizations.

Lee Harvey Oswald, who was unquestionably pro-Castro and pro-communist, did not try especially hard at this new job, however, not because he was aware of the company's anti-Castro disposition but because he knew he did not need to work there long.

As Oswald walked home from work after his first day, a man reading a gun magazine while leaning against a car at the garage next door to Reily Coffee Co., greeted him and struck up a conversation about an open page in his magazine. They talked for a few short minutes about each other's military experience and the guns they owned or had used in the military, until finally the man extended his hand, expecting a handshake from Oswald, and said, "Hey, I'm Adrian Alba, by the way."

"Lee. Lee Oswald. Hello, it's very nice to meet you." His words seemed a little awkward as they had already been standing there carrying on a conversation for a few minutes, but he accepted the man's handshake.

"Well, I need to close up shop and head for da house. You can borrow that magazine if you want."

"Thanks, I will! I'll drop it back by tomorrow."

As Alba walked away, he threw a response over his shoulder. "Plenty more where that one came from!"

Oswald rolled up the magazine, slipped it into his back pocket, and began the three-and-a-half-mile walk home through the

Warehouse and Garden Districts of the older part of New Orleans.

Over the next few weeks, Oswald spent quite a bit of time at the garage talking to Alba about guns and gun magazines. Oswald *was* too gullible and egocentric to realize that Alba was examining and analyzing him to find out how much he really knew about guns and ammunition, and what kind of guns Oswald already owned or which he could get him to purchase. When Alba felt he had learned all he was able to, the Reily Coffee Co. used the fact that Oswald was next door talking far too often instead of working to terminate his employment.

1963, June 11, The White House

Speaking from behind the presidential podium at the White House, Kennedy gave an eloquent speech on civil rights. The points he so clearly articulated had good intentions, although he repeatedly stated that all *men* ought to have equal rights and opportunities. The effort he made to promote equality for all was valiant indeed, if not overdue by lifetimes. However, yet again, large numbers of people were angry with JFK.

Many African Americans were furious because they believed Kennedy was not doing enough for civil rights, even though practically everyone in America knew that, earlier in the day, Kennedy had personally ordered the Alabama National Guard to the University of Alabama to see to the safety of the university's first two African American students.

"All men are equal" was a step in the right direction, but those words were weak compared to "racism and hatred will no longer be tolerated."

Civil rights leaders, including Michael "Martin Luther" King Jr., believed that the president of the United States should force businesses to remove the "Whites Only" signs and give African Americans the same education opportunities as white males. Baby steps were not sufficient. Huge strides were needed for African Americans.

White supremacists were livid with Kennedy as well. Hundreds, possibly thousands, of white racists swore they were going to kill that such-and-such-loving so-and-so before he destroyed America if it was the last thing they ever did.

Many young women, blinded by Kennedy's good looks, charm, and power, overlooked his blunder of singling out men as being equal while disregarding women altogether. This oversight enraged many other women, though, or made them feel disenfranchised. The women's movement for equal rights also became stronger and more outspoken.

A handful of these civil rights leaders organized thousands more like-minded women, gathering at several places all over the United States to protest.

Contrary to urban legend, however, these protestors did *not* burn their bras in protest, although a few might have been angry enough to want to burn the ones they perceived were suppressing their rights and freedoms.

Reelection season had already begun, so some of JFK's fellow politicians began to distance themselves from him as well, fearful of the reactions of their constituents. All the equal rights talk and discontent with Kennedy had politicians incorrectly assuming that the *loudest* voices they heard represented *most* of the voices. They did not, yet former JFK supporters now publicly disagreed, thinking that they had better act in a way that would get them the most votes at the next election.

Willing to say anything to be reelected, they supported the status quo on civil rights instead of supporting their president's charge to promote equal rights. Fewer politicians supported the equal rights movement because of Kennedy's Equal Rights speech, in effect, portraying the message that no change was necessary. The silent majority remained unheard, but understood that when JFK said "all men," he meant "all mankind." Or at least all Americans.

Many business owners and executives were already irritated at the Kennedy administration over other issues that had forced them to be more accountable for their actions. When they heard about JFK's new civil rights initiatives, they were further angered. Equal rights would mean equal pay. They would be forced to either give many employees a raise or pay their white male employees less.

A surprising number of small business owners were still reluctant to take down the “Whites Only” signs from their establishments. Decades would pass before the last of those signs were removed.

No matter how hard Kennedy tried to make life better for his fellow Americans, he very rarely said *any*thing that did not anger one or more groups of people.

1963, Early July, New Orleans

Loud music drowned out the numerous conversations taking place at a strip club in the French Quarter. Nude women "danced" in several makeshift cages on four stages specifically designed to maximize the view from all sides and angles. The music and nudity provided additional distractions for a particularly intense conversation taking place in one of the back corners of the club.

Three men with fat Cuban cigars sat at a round table, somehow managing to position themselves so that no one had his back turned to the rest of the club, or each other.

Most of the other patrons were regulars and recognized one of the men well enough to know to stay away when he was meeting with people, so the surrounding tables and booths were empty. Anyone close enough to see the three men through the thick smoke, and brave enough to look in their direction, might be able to read lips well enough to make out an occasional "Kennedy" or "Bobby" uttered with hatred by any of the three, or the name "Hoffa" spoken by Frank Ragano.

1963, Mid-July, The White House

On the lawn of the White House, Robert F. Kennedy was obviously distressed. "Jack, look, Hoover claims the press has it all. The naked pool parties, Norma Jeane, Ellen, *and* Fiddle and Faddle. They even know how much we pay the girls and how we get them in and out of he-ah."

Robert F. Kennedy stood with his arms folded across his chest like his big brother. "The boys wouldn't have done this, and I don't think any of them have all the details Hoover says they have. One of the 'ladies' *had* to have talked to them. Goddamnit, Jack, he says Ellen is most likely an East German *spy*!"

Squirming uncomfortably from either the constant pain in his back or the subject at hand, or both, Kennedy thought, *A goddamn commie spy!* But looking his brother in the eye, he said, "Bobby, I am *not* going to tolerate another press shitstorm."

The president spoke in hushed yet forceful tones. "Do whatever you feel is necessary to keep this out of the papers. Have Hoover assign someone to these assholes immediately. Find something on them. *Any*thing that will persuade them to..." Jack paused for a split second longer than he would have if his back had not been bothering him, "...find oth-ah stories that the general public might like to read about their president."

Bobby noted that his older brother and president refused to acknowledge the disturbing news that he could be fooling around with a communist spy.

They both stepped back inside the White House without another word. Bobby plopped down in one of the new easy chairs Jackie had picked out for them, snatched up a phone, and continued his never-ending job of cleanup and damage control. Jack placed a call as well, to Dr. Max Jacobson to make immediate arrangements for another injection of amphetamines to help ease the severe pain in his back.

Less than two hours later, a single CIA agent threatened three reporters. One of the journalists was clearly frightened, another was wide-eyed and open-mouthed, staring in disbelief. The third reporter made the mistake of becoming a little too belligerent. The agent walked over and whispered an all-too-believable threat in the man's ear.

The reporter was no longer rebellious and now appeared to be as frightened as his fellow journalists. "How do *you* know what my father, uh, oh, right. CIA. The CIA." The reporter's eyes told the agent everything he needed to know, so he walked away confident that he had stopped yet another story from embarrassing his president, and therefore America.

One of the three correspondents simply remained standing there with his jaw dropped, staring incredulously, and another literally shook from fear. The third reporter was furious, however, and was already plotting his revenge for the threat against his father. For the first time in his adult life, the longtime journalist questioned which might truly be mightier—the pen or the sword.

Years passed before the general public found out about Jack Kennedy's long line of prostitutes and assorted girlfriends. A *parade* of women known to be operating outside of the law had direct and repeated access to the president of the United States.

Everyone else who wanted or needed access had to go through a rigorous screening process to have the ear of the highest-ranking official in America, and arguably the world. These girls were common hookers, yet their backgrounds and motives were rarely questioned. The prostitutes who became regulars, like Fiddle and Faddle, were ushered into the presence of the president so often that the Secret Service often didn't even bother to search them.

The average American didn't know about the easy, backdoor access to their president. If the Kennedy brothers' infidelities were to become public knowledge, there was little doubt there would be a resounding demand for that to stop immediately. However, more than a handful of people who were perhaps the most loyal civil servants in America *did* know. They knew because they were the Secret Service agents making it happen for the Kennedys, quietly escorting the prostitutes in and out of the White House, or in and out of wherever they happened to be staying. If even *one* of these men suspected that a spy had easy access to their president, they would *all* know about it very quickly.

Everyone knows what people who consider themselves to be true patriots are capable of doing in the name of America and freedom.

1963, July 25, New Orleans

Though Lee Harvey Oswald had spent a third of his childhood and adolescence in New Orleans, it seemed that any acclimation he had developed to the heat, humidity, and sweat back then had long since diminished. He was sweaty and uncomfortable, and even though the fan was on high, it wasn't doing much other than redistributing the muggy air around the room.

A mess on the kitchen table forced Oswald to spread his work out on his bed again. The one-room apartment did not have sufficient space for a desk, and the housekeeper wasn't due to come by and clean for two more days. He never even considered cleaning the mess himself, but having the housekeeper come *twice* a week wasn't possible anymore since he lost another job about a week earlier. He really didn't have money for a housekeeper at all, but people all have different priorities.

Oswald tossed the phone book and a large envelope onto the bed, found a pen in the mess on the table, and flopped down on the bed, knocking a stack of socialist publications and a Kennedy biography onto the floor. Oblivious to this new mess, he began his weekly ritual of finding businesses in the phone book to enter into his unemployment compensation claim form. He looked for businesses that he might know a little something about, so he could invent a set of convincing lies about each. He had become an expert at answering any of the questions the unemployment office workers might have for him.

Before Oswald could finish filling out his fictitious unemployment application, he heard the mail carrier rattling the tin mailbox of the house next door. Hurrying to his own mailbox, already expecting his weekly unemployment check, he found instead a letter from the United States Marine Corps denying his request to overturn the decision to designate his military discharge status as Undesirable.

"Damn bureaucrats. 'Careful consideration' my ass!" Oswald wanted to wad the letter and yell at someone. Had his wife been there, he would surely have been yelling at her. Instead, he focused his hatred on the person he had asked to provide him with a full review of his discharge status, John Connally, who had been the secretary of the Navy at the time he made the request.

Connally had been the governor of Texas since January, and was now also the center of Oswald's loathing and anger. His intense, misguided odium of authority was so overwhelming that it continued to consume him.

1963, July 31, CIA Headquarters

George Efthyron Joannides bounced around in a rough taxi ride on his way to a meeting, staring absentmindedly out of the rear passenger window, lost in thought. It was not unusual for him to travel from his office in Miami to CIA Headquarters in Virginia, *however*, it did seem a little odd that they would request his presence merely for a yearly job evaluation. He could think of no reason to worry, but still, one had to wonder why they would want him to travel all that way, unless it was to deliver bad news.

Thinking back, he did a quick assessment of his own performance. He had advanced through the ranks rapidly to become the Chief of Psychological Warfare Operations in Miami, so he felt he must be doing *something* correctly. While performing the duties of chief, which he took very seriously, he had done his best to develop and maintain an onslaught of harassment tactics aimed toward Fidel Castro and a small portion of the Cuban population in Florida.

One of the many tactics he had found effective was supporting the DRE, which was a contentious element in Cuba, with organizational offices located in Miami, New Orleans, and several other cities in the Americas. Angry young students could be a powerful weapon to wield, and the Directorio Revolucionario Estudiantil, that is, the (Cuban) Revolutionary Student Directorate, provided such an opportunity.

There was one issue about supporting the DRE that was now giving Joannides reason to pause—the DRE was a self-described *militant* right-wing, anti-communist, anti-Castro, *anti-Kennedy* group. For the first time, he was beginning to question if he still supported such tactics, or if those efforts had turned on him and attacked him like an abused dog.

Joannides also contemplated if his practice of spending thousands of dollars per week on weapons and supplies for Cuban exiles and other potential rebels had itself become contentious. Perhaps spending the majority of his time on this one endeavor had turned into something worrisome, or even unfavorable.

With the rough cab ride over, and no more time for second-guessing himself, Joannides made his way directly to his meeting, his only stop being one of opportunity as he passed a pot of notoriously bad, not-so-fresh, extra-strong coffee.

Less than three hours later, with his job evaluation behind him, Joannides' cab ride back to the airport was far less stressful. The ride even seemed smoother, although he was sure that was just his imagination.

Apparently, all those in charge were quite pleased with his efforts in Miami. They had given him the highest assessment possible and had officially given him credit for establishing a unique and effective control over the DRE. They wanted him to continue to work toward assisting the students, exiles, and anyone else who might be interested to prepare for and spark another Cuban revolution.

Joannides went back to Miami rededicated to his efforts, determined not to let anything, or anyone, interfere with the CIA's attempts to kindle unrest in Cuba while inflicting as much psychological harm as their considerable budget would allow.

1963, Early August, Dallas

Jack Ruby had a handful of bills and final notices in his hands, and a faraway look in his eyes. An overwhelming sense of desperation and anxiety had been creeping over him since he realized one of the letters he received that morning was from the IRS. He stared at the dreaded numbers on the first page while the sickening feeling of dread in his gut slowly turned into the kind of stress that gave so many middle-aged men heart attacks.

The only thing Ruby's eyes could seem to focus on were the words "tax lien" and a dollar amount equal to four or five times what he was then making in an entire year.

Since the day he sold the last cache of rifles to his connections in Cuba, the bills had been piling up. The nightclub business was not doing nearly as well as his books had been showing for the past few years. The "supplemental income" he made arranging sales of weapons to hopeful Cuban rebels was considerably more than merely supplemental. It accounted for three-quarters of his income.

Ruby's mind raced through numerous possibilities and options, nearly all of which involved doing rash things for sinister "friends" in Chicago and New Orleans. He didn't want to go down that road. He wanted *them* to come to *him* if they ever needed anything in Dallas. They never had, of course, but captivated as he was by his self-aggrandizement, he was always open to the possibility.

At this time, however, Ruby needed those gangsters. And he realized that he was willing to do just about anything to solve his financial dilemma. He knew if he did nothing, he would lose not only the business he had operated for so many years but also his livelihood. He understood the potential was low for an older man to find a job that paid enough to live on, and the fact that he would be out of work because his *strip club* had failed would not be a favorable point in making him more employable.

Additionally, it was obvious that if he asked for help from mobsters, he would owe them for life, regardless of whether they came through for him and offered him a job of some kind. He felt trapped, with few options left open for him, none of them at all desirable.

1963, August 5, New Orleans

Lee Harvey Oswald felt a burning need for people to believe he was a man of great importance. He often tried to associate with people or organizations he believed would elevate his lowly status into something more consequential.

Becoming noteworthy or significant in history was very important to him, or at least being in the spotlight and center stage of newsworthy current events for a time until he gained enough notoriety to be well known. Even while performing ordinary, day-to-day tasks, if he believed he were not going to get what he felt entitled to receive, he would attempt to go straight to the top of the business, institution, or establishment instead of asking for a manager or supervisor.

Oswald visited Carlos José Bringuier, the Cuban in charge of the New Orleans Revolutionary Student Directorate office because he had studied law at the University of Havana in the mid-1950s. However, Oswald did not contact him at his office, but instead chose to confront him at the Casa Roca clothing store that Bringuier managed. Oswald assumed that this setting was more likely to give him the upper hand he craved, and would allow him to be more in control. If his efforts to infiltrate the Revolutionary Student Directorate failed, he could at least put the man's job in jeopardy.

Tending to business at the Casa Roca, Bringuier noticed a young white male enter his store. Their customer base was strictly Hispanic, and almost exclusively Cuban, so Bringuier's suspicion was aroused.

Hearing the *Americano* ask for him specifically, he assumed something underhanded was about to occur. The only white man with whom he freely associated was a CIA agent, and that was more out of necessity than anything else, *and* he was from Greece, not America. Somehow this fact comforted him and allowed him to ignore his own principles enough to tolerate that particular white man's presence.

Two men with radically different ideas about race, communism, and Castro shook hands, each doing his best to conceal the deep-rooted contempt and resentment they had for each other. Bringuier disliked Oswald because he was white, and Oswald disliked Bringuier because of his rejection of communism.

Oswald rearranged his facial expression into something that he felt might portray importance and got right to the point.

"I hate Castro and all he stands for. I hate communism, and I hate the fact that it is alive and well in our own back yard."

"Castro is indeed, ah, *uno hombre malo*. One bad hombre."

"Yes, sir, he is." Redirecting the conversation to where he wanted it to go, Oswald flippantly added, "They say you are the man to see in New Orleans if you are against Castro and communism."

Bringuier resisted the urge to ask who "they" were, but sensed that the gringo was lying to him now. Realizing that asking questions would simply produce more lies, he quickly decided to offer Oswald some Revolutionary Student Directorate pamphlets in hopes that he would simply go away. No such luck.

Slipping the leaflets into his back pocket without even giving them a glance, Oswald continued the charade, knowing that the best lies always contain at least some truth.

"I was in the Marine Corps where I received intense and thorough special ops training in guerrilla warfare." Oswald paused to see if the Cuban was at all impressed. He obviously was not, so he continued. "I am willing to help the DRE train Cubans to fight against Castro and the evil that has engulfed Cuba."

“Is that right?” Bringuier certainly did not believe the gringo, but he had to admit that he was beginning to doubt his mistrust. The thought of using some of Uncle Sam’s own citizens to overthrow Castro was appealing.

Oswald sensed the shift in Bringuier’s posture. “And I am willing to go there myself, to help with the fighting.” The spark of suspicion in Bringuier’s eye dulled another fraction, so Oswald tried to seal the deal with the mention of a genuine interest in purchasing bonds that might help their cause. They both knew that these types of bonds were illegal and currently under intense scrutiny, so the ember of distrust in Bringuier’s eyes began to glow brighter.

The men parted ways, unsure of each other. Oswald went home to dig out his old Marines training manual, *Guidebook for Marines*.

When Oswald stopped back by the Casa Roca the next day to show Bringuier his Marines training manual, he discovered he was not there, so he left the manual with Bringuier’s subordinates with instructions for someone to give him the manual at the earliest opportunity.

1963, August 9, New Orleans

Walking up and down Canal Street, Oswald was offering "Fair Play for Cuba" fliers to anyone who would accept them and spouting verbal information to anyone he thought might be listening. Although a few people took the fliers, most of the pedestrians politely refused or ignored him completely. Many who accepted the fliers dropped them onto the sidewalk as soon as they realized they were reading "literature" that supported Castro and communism.

Intending to cover the entire area surrounding the Casa Roca clothing store, Oswald canvassed some of Canal Street's intersecting and adjacent streets, such as Camp, Common, and Tchoupitoulas Streets. He hoped someone would alert Bringuier that there was a pro-Castro antagonist passing out "Fair Play for Cuba" fliers right there in his own neighborhood.

It took far longer than Oswald had imagined, but eventually Bringuier showed up with two other Cuban exiles, Miguel Cruz and Celso Hernandez, who had first noticed Oswald and reported it to Bringuier.

Exhibiting the most irritating smirk he could produce, Oswald reveled in satisfaction as he saw the surprise on Bringuier's face. He knew the anti-Castro Cuban exile recognized the man who had been in his store a few days earlier. Surprise turned to anger as Bringuier realized that Oswald had been trying to play him and infiltrate the DRE. His suspicions had been correct.

Bringuier quickly drew a crowd with common anti-communist rhetoric and expertly turned the congregation into an angry mob against Oswald. In only a couple of minutes, he had them shouting and cursing the commie, but Oswald continued smirking and even taunted the Cuban. A New Orleans police officer showed up and arrested all four men before the row could turn into a scuffle.

Oswald smirked and stared down Bringuier even as he held his arms out, wrists together, to the officer in an “arrest me” gesture. All four were jailed and charged with Disturbing the Peace.

Less than twenty-four hours later, in Miami, Joannides was upset. One of his most useful chess pieces now had a criminal record, *and,* to make matters worse, this Oswald fellow had been running his mouth about the activities of the DRE to the FBI! He was *not* going to allow some insignificant, inconsequential *juvenile* to impede his efforts to stop the spread of communism.

1963, September 26–October 3, Mexico City

Someone using the name Lee Oswald visited Mexico City for a week. This thirty-five-year-old balding man was taller than Oswald and even dressed nicer than the typical Oswald attire. The imposter entered the Mexico City Soviet Embassy several times to make phone calls. Surveillance cameras captured images of him, which confirmed that he was not Oswald.

1963, October 5, *Christina*

Aboard the *Christina*, Aristotle Onassis' luxury yacht, Jackie exclaimed, "Oh, Ari, she's beautiful!"

"There is nothing like her afloat anywhere in the world."

Jacqueline Kennedy walked arm in arm with Aristotle Onassis, recently divorced, on an upper deck of what was, without question, the finest privately owned yacht anywhere on the planet. They made idle chitchat while strolling through areas of the ship he imagined might be interesting to the president's wife. At each stop, he transformed himself from the role of gracious host to that of a tour guide, explaining the importance or function of each point of interest in excruciating detail.

In the pristine bridge, the first officer called him "sir" with perhaps a touch of dramatics, and Mrs. Kennedy was, of course, aware that Mr. Onassis hadn't a clue what all the gauges and controls did. On a mid-level deck was an indoor pool surrounded with luxurious lounge chairs grouped together in romantic pairs, separated by potted plants and folding bamboo walls. The kitchen was well equipped and bustling, and a sundeck had a "simply mah-velous" view of the bay.

The *Christina* was truly impressive, but near the end of the tour, in the privacy of the captain's quarters, "Ari" skillfully turned the conversation to the problem he had with Jackie's husband—or at least the only problem he had with her husband that he was willing to share with her.

"Jackie, he wrote Salinger's speech. He knew all too well that no one has 'secured' this craft from me. It was nothing but a vicious, cruel insult meant to be a threat to me—and my manhood. He is a child, Jackie, envious of the wealth and power I have gained without having to answer to sniveling, incompetent voters."

Jackie didn't know what to say. She had never thought of her husband's power quite the way Onassis had described it. She had to admit to herself that the notion of fame and fortune she preferred was more like that which Onassis enjoyed rather than the public life she must share as America's First Lady. She did not really pay much attention to the speech Pierre Salinger had given the previous week, although with her host's reminder, she recalled hearing that a prince or some other royalty had secured the yacht from Onassis. That statement did seem out of place and context now that she was giving it some thought.

Why would her friend give up his yacht the same week they had scheduled a cruise to Athens? Then it dawned on her that Jack was jealous. Just because he was the president of the United States didn't mean he had left his ego back in Boston. The very idea of her husband being jealous was ludicrous to her. Him! Jealous of her! She was aware of his womanizing, or at least some of it, so the thought of him being jealous over this perfectly innocent cruise seemed ridiculous.

Understandably lost in her own private thoughts for a moment, she snapped back to reality when she was startled by hearing Ari blurt out awkwardly, "Leave him, Jackie, and marry me."

Mrs. Kennedy was stunned but responded in a casual tone that was uniquely Jacqueline Bouvier Kennedy, "Gracious, Ari, what would people think?"

As intended, the man didn't feel hurt or rejected, yet neither did he receive an answer to his proposal. Momentarily perplexed, the resentment and hatred (and envy) he held for the president subsided while he basked in the glory of not being shunned by one of the most beautiful women he had ever seen.

The bliss in which he was awash lasted only a short time, however. He was soon dwelling again on his hatred of John F. Kennedy. In his mind, he knew he would have Jackie. He didn't know it would take five years and a few days, but he knew he would have her, and he began forming his plans as they finished the tour of his yacht.

1963, October 7, The White House

On national television, Kennedy exhaled a sigh of relief as he finished signing the Treaty Banning Nuclear Weapon Tests in the Atmosphere, in Outer Space, and Under Water, more commonly known as the Partial Test Ban Treaty. Most American citizens were as relieved as their president that nuclear weapons testing would come to an end, at least for the time being.

However, as with many decisions Kennedy made during his presidency, a portion of Americans were outraged. They believed the treaty was more about backing down from an imminent threat. Even some of the few remaining military leaders he had yet to anger were troubled by the treaty, thinking that it weakened America's defense unnecessarily.

Even though the United States Senate had ratified the treaty more than two weeks earlier, many people felt as though the decision was wholly Kennedy's. Any disadvantages of the treaty, real or imagined, were perceived as being entirely the fault of their president.

Many defense industry leaders and investors blamed and detested President Kennedy for this treaty, as well. They felt as though they had much to gain financially when the world was constantly on the brink of World War III. The United States defense industry could not turn a profit, or even stay in business, without dangerous enemies threatening the rest of the world with weapons of mass destruction.

Defense industry executives understood enough about greed and human nature to know better than to believe that the superpowers of the world would ever live free of conflict. They knew that peace wouldn't break out any time during their lifetimes or the lifetimes of their children and grandchildren. They also believed that the leader of the free world should know this better than anyone.

No matter how many peace treaties were agreed upon and signed, no matter how many enemy states were resourcefully converted into lasting friendships, and no matter how optimistic the future might look, friends turned on one another far too often. The "friend" who maintained the best defenses during the peaceful years was surely going to be the one who perpetuated *their* way of life. However, when friendships failed, and one country turned on another, the weakest of them stood a good chance of suffering unrecoverable losses.

A small percentage of the outraged defense industry investors were distraught about what their president was doing to their beloved country. A handful of them were angry enough to plot amongst themselves.

Many of these investors didn't invest in the defense industry because of the profit margin, which was not always great. There were much more lucrative investment opportunities available if turning a profit was the only motivating factor. Most of them were making these hefty investments into their nation's defense because they felt it was very important to their future and to the future of their families. They were making money from these investments, but not nearly as much as they could be making had they invested in other endeavors.

Similarly, the individuals in the upper management positions of the defense industry could have made a much higher salary in a similar position in the private sector, yet they continued to work for lower pay because they wanted America's defense to be the best it could possibly be. To see years, or even decades of efforts seemingly undermined by the president was too much for some of them.

Hatred derived from the perception of betrayal and from a threatened future swelled in their hearts. Their minds were driven to think of ingenious ways to remove the threat without getting their own hands dirty.

Many of the big business executives who were *not* in the defense industry were cashing in on as many moneymaking opportunities as the *war* in Vietnam could present. In every soldier's pack of rations was the standard pack of cigarettes, at least until 1972. American taxpayers purchased all these cigarettes, even though the packs were the *sample four-packs* that tobacco companies gave away by the thousands at promotions and, believe it or not, at medical and public *health* meetings until the early 1960s.

Matches, chewing gum, plastic utensils, coffee, and sugar (no longer purchased from Cuba) were all bought with taxes and war bonds. But *all* of it was overpriced simply because the vendors were selling to the U.S. government—even though everyone else received discounts for purchasing in bulk.

Beloved companies like Coca-Cola supported war efforts too, since World War I proved that more of their products sold while wars were raging. Wars also served to introduce more American products to foreign countries than any other means. Coca-Cola was no exception. Many businesses wanted the U.S. government to send some of their customers overseas to die so that they could sell more products to new and surviving customers.

1963, Mid-October, The Oval Office

"Wait! Stop right the-ah. That son of a bitch said *what*?"

Robert F. Kennedy looked up over the intelligence report that was supposed to summarize the past few weeks of activities of the president of South Vietnam, Ngo Dinh Diem. Mimicking the expression on his brother's face momentarily, Bobby looked back at the report, found the quote, and repeated it, adding, "Quote, unquote," while glancing up again.

"'We Catholics must unite against the filthy Buddhists who have nothing better to do but to prevent us from world domination.'"

Shaking his head, Jack responded, "If Lyndon were he-ah, he'd say, 'Aw, hell!'" Disgusted, the first-ever Catholic president requested that his brother "go on" with the report.

"Well, apparently Diem is doing his best to provoke the Buddhists into an uprising, but if they demonstrate even the least bit of dissidence, he uses that as an excuse to arrest them, and has even *killed* scores of them already." Over the past two years, Bobby had learned how to read a large amount of information and easily summarize it so that his brother could make decisions quickly. The forty-some-odd-page report became a seven-minute conversation.

"Nepotism, widespread government corruption, severely failing land reforms, and alienating every Buddhist in Southeast Asia have most of the South Vietnamese hating him *and* hating us for supporting him. The Buddhists in South Vietnam are supporting Ho Chi Minh more and more.

"Diem has also been losing support among the citizens of most other countries as well. Viet Cong guerrillas are getting to be more and more commonplace, and the June incident of his orders to machine-gun temples and unarmed citizens simply will not be forgotten. Diem and his brother are now resentful toward the U.S. for cutting off aid in response to their atrocities. They're actually surprised we didn't support them."

"Get with Henry. Have him refuse to meet with Diem until he shows more willingness to represent *all* his citizens. Somehow, we have to get control of the situation over the-ah, Bobby. Whatever it takes."

Robert put the report face down on a table and made a quick note on the back. Then he leaned back and propped one leg up over the other. "Well, Mr. President, how serious are you about that?"

"Deadly serious." After thinking for a split second, the president shot his younger brother a cockeyed glance. "Why?"

"General Dương Van Minh is reportedly leading another coup attempt against Diem."

The president of the United States thought about the ramifications of this scenario while his attorney general sat in silence, knowing not to interrupt. Bobby had too much of his own thinking to do anyway.

"Get *unofficial* word to the general. If he can pull off a bloodless coup, we won't oppose or interfe-ah in its operation. Bobby, make sure he knows that only *if* he can remove the Ngo Dinhs without spilling a drop of blood will we support the new government officials."

1963, October 16, Dallas

Oswald had endured many frustrating weeks of one disappointment and setback after another, including separating from his wife, again, losing jobs, having visas rejected by both Cuba and Russia, *again*, and moving to New Orleans briefly, only to spend a night in jail for fighting with an anti-Castro activist.

He had also recently learned that the Marines still refused to overturn his Undesirable Discharge, which had been hampering his ability to land a viable job.

That morning, however, the tide seemed to be turning for Oswald. He was in a good mood, for he was beginning his new job at the Texas School Book Depository, which overlooks Dealey Plaza on the west side of Dallas.

1963, November 1, Beverly Hills

Diem's sister-in-law, Madame Nhu (Nhu's wife) was considered Vietnam's First Lady, as Diem had never married. Less affectionately, she was also known as "Dragon Lady" for openly enjoying what she described as "monk barbecue shows."

The "shows" she referred to were protesting Buddhist priests who would sit cross-legged in the street, usually in front of one of their temples. They then doused their heavy robes with gasoline and waited for a crowd to gather. When enough people had stopped to see another spectacle, they would set themselves ablaze.

Dragon Lady witnessed a few of the monk suicides, where she pushed her way to the front of the crowd and watched with obvious delight. As the burning monks gasped searing flames into their lungs and allowed themselves to burn to death, she applauded enthusiastically.

As if she wasn't detested enough, she was also the granddaughter of the hated Emperor Dong Khanh. Madame Nhu also worked feverishly to impose her unpopular "Morality Laws" upon the South Vietnamese population. Most of "her" citizens could live with the majority of the laws, such as banning animal fighting and opium dens, but most of the Vietnamese people did not wish to be told that they could not get a divorce. Contraceptives were not popular, but few wanted to be told they could not use them if they wished. Dance halls *were* quite popular, but her Morality Laws banned those, too.

Madame Nhu listened to no one and forged on, selflessly in her mind, selfishly through the eyes of everyone else.

While her South Vietnamese countrymen suffered from the effects of long-term war, Madame Nhu had shamelessly shopped nonstop in Beverly Hills, California, since her October 13 appearance on *Meet the Press.*

The day of shopping was no different on November 1, 1963, except that her daughter, Ngo Le Thuy, was accompanying her. They leisurely spent other people's money in shops and on dining in fine restaurants, neither of them concerned that the thousands of dollars they were squandering had been intended to be aid and relief for the suffering of the South Vietnamese people.

The money Madame Nhu spent on a single outfit at a high-end store could have bought food for an *entire* village, for an *entire* month. The mother and daughter shared the same sense of entitlement that allowed them to spend the cash as if the United States owed them the money for simply being who they were.

While they were shopping and gleefully squandering much of the relief funds, Madame Nhu's husband and brother-in-law were being targeted in a coup.

Meanwhile, President Kennedy had attended one conference after another, all day long, and had fielded a barrage of phone calls from contacts all over Vietnam and the surrounding area. His staff was constantly updating him, interrupting each other frequently about one new situation or another as one of the most historically significant events in Southeast Asia unfolded.

Henry Cabot Lodge Jr., now the Kennedy-appointed ambassador to South Vietnam, was in Southeast Asia briefing General Paul D. Harkins on the imminent coup while, not far away, President Ngo Dinh Diem hung up a telephone and turned to his brother. "Inevitable." Nhu nodded. "Our 'friends' in the White House have betrayed us and are now our enemies." Diem immediately ordered his loyalists to exit Gia Long Palace en masse.

Diem's troops escorted him and Nhu to a Catholic church in the Cholon district of Saigon. There, with the help of some misinformation/disinformation from a loyal security chief, they plotted several misleading story lines and arranged for several loyalists to "leak" the stories to various key people they knew were incapable of keeping information confidential. They knew that the more credible misleading stories they disseminated, the better their chances would be of getting out of Vietnam alive.

Later that night, a tracked and armored M113 personnel carrier roared into the district, stirring up a choking cloud of dust. As the dust settled, a solitary, trusted U.S. Army grunt climbed out and met a haggard CIA agent and a crusty old South Vietnamese general outside the church. The two ordered the soldier to deliver Diem and his brother Nhu to the Joint General Staff (JGS) immediately.

The CIA agent drilled the orders into the grunt's head. "Nothing is to deter the soldier from the mission. Nothing. No matter what happens, at any given time, he is to go directly to the Joint General Staff headquarters, or indirectly if the direct route becomes impossible to traverse, deliver the two people about to be loaded into his transport, and simply report to his superiors that Ngo Dinh Diem and Ngo Dinh Nhu had, in fact, been delivered to them."

Not confused by the CIA agent addressing him as a third party, the grunt shouted as if he were back in boot camp. "Sir, yes, sir!"

"Furthermore, the Army grunt is to say nothing else about his orders to anyone. Ever. Nothing about who gave the orders or anything he witnessed. He is to say only what he has been ordered to say."

"Sir, yes, sir!"

"No matter what."

The browbeating continued until the CIA agent was sure that nothing would deter the man's mind from his mission. Then he waved to someone in the doorway of the church, who turned and nodded to someone else, inside. Four Vietnamese soldiers carried two bloody, dead bodies out of the church and placed them inside the transport.

Diem and Nhu watched from inside the church. The driver of the transport showed no reaction or emotion, although he was in complete disbelief. Two innocent bystanders were killed in cold blood so that Diem and Nhu could live. He stood at attention until the CIA agent looked at him again and said, “Dismissed,” through clenched teeth.

The driver climbed aboard the transport, fired up the tracked beast, and headed for JGS in another cloud of dust and foul black exhaust.

As soon as the transport was out of sight, the spook turned to the two ousted leaders in the window and gave them a long, stoic stare. Without so much as a nod, he and the South Vietnamese general climbed into an unmarked French vehicle and drove away.

A few minutes later, after driving a couple of “klicks” out of Cholon, the CIA agent turned off the headlights and pulled his 9mm out of its holster as he stopped dead in the middle of the road. He peered into the darkness in front of him, as if he were trying to make out some shadowy figure lurking out in the darkness.

The Vietnamese general in the seat next to him also leaned forward, squinting to see what might lie ahead. The CIA agent quickly shot a bullet into the temple of his “comrade.” He then backed the car into a turnoff and parked beside another unmarked car. Using enough gasoline to burn an entire fleet of cars, he set the French vehicle ablaze by tossing a lit Zippo lighter into the driver’s seat. He stayed long enough to confirm that the general’s body was beginning to burn in the inferno, then climbed into the other car and drove away.

Burning dead bodies was a common enough occurrence for him to not be disturbed by it. At all.

Over a period of fifty hours, presidential aides offered an exhausted Kennedy differing reports of the progress of the coup in Saigon. A memorandum from the CIA shocked everyone in the Oval Office. U.S. Army and Vietnamese sources reported that Diem and his brother had both committed suicide after initially escaping the coup.

Further reports revealed that Diem and his brother were found in the back of a U.S. Army personnel transport with their hands bound behind their backs. They had apparently committed suicide by either shooting or stabbing themselves, or each other, multiple times. A search of the vehicle produced no suicide weapons, and the driver, who had the complete trust of his commanding officer, admitted that he had Saigon Radio blaring most of the way from Cholon to Joint General Staff headquarters.

One of the last reports Kennedy read before finally succumbing to the need for sleep was about Madame Nhu. A Secret Service agent following her reported that she had made several threatening remarks aimed at the Kennedy administration and felt as though Kennedy was personally responsible for the deaths of her husband and brother.

Despite the many threats on the president that she had made in public and to the news networks, the media ignored these remarks and focused the bulk of their reports on one single quote from Dragon Lady: "Whoever has Americans as allies does not need enemies."

Also largely ignored by the media were the countless atrocities committed by Diem and his brother, and why Madame Nhu was nicknamed Dragon Lady. Instead, the media chose the more sensationalist approach of making American leadership look bad.

Headlines, magazines, and television news anchors alike seized upon the “does not need enemies” quote and pounded away at it for days, drilling it into the minds of all who read or watched the news. People responded to the sensationalism, so the media gave them more. Meanwhile, network viewership was up, and newspaper and magazine sales continued to increase.

1963, November 19, Texas School Book Depository

Lee Harvey Oswald sat in the break room of the Texas School Book Depository resentfully eating a sandwich that he felt should have been made by his wife. Every bite made him dwell on different ways he might convince her to reunite their family.

His heart hurt because he had barely spent any time with their newborn, Audrey, who was only hours away from being a month old. Oswald felt helpless knowing he had no control over their on-again, off-again living arrangements. The frustration swelled, but he just sat eating his lunch, knowing he couldn't do anything about it.

Another School Book Depository employee having lunch at another table noticed Lee's obvious discomfort and exited the break room, leaving his *Dallas Times Herald* scattered all over the table where he had been sitting.

Oswald moved to that table and began scanning the newspaper in an attempt to distract himself from the mess that was his life. Mindlessly turning the pages, looking for something that might interest him, he saw the article that officially notified the public of the presidential motorcade route that would be rolling through the area the following Friday. He immediately noticed that the parade would drive right under the windows that overlooked Dealey Plaza.

1963, November 21, Texas School Book Depository

Oswald asked coworker Buell Wesley Frazier for another ride to the Paine's home, who lived near Buell in the city of Irving. Being a Thursday, this was a little out of the ordinary. Since Oswald had separated from his wife, Marina, he usually stayed in his room at the boarding house on week nights and only went to the Paine's on weekends to visit his wife and daughters. When Buell asked about this, Oswald explained.

"Marina has made me some curtains, and I'm going out to get some curtain rods so I can put curtains up in my room at the boarding house."

Buell wondered why he didn't ask to be dropped off at a department store, but did not ask why. He did not want Oswald to take him up on the offer and then ask him to wait while he purchased curtain rods.

1963, November 22, Irving and Dallas

Oswald never slept well on the Paine's couch. The previous night was no exception. He slipped into Marina's bedroom and watched her sleep for a few moments. After some reflection, he slipped off his wedding ring and placed it in a cup on her dresser.

Another look at his Soviet wife prompted him to pull the wallet from his back pocket and remove $170, which he quietly placed in one of the dresser drawers. That left him with less than $20.

Without disturbing anyone, he retrieved his rifle from the Paine's garage and walked the few blocks to the Frazier's home with the firearm wrapped in the brown wrapping paper that he took from work.

Buell had left his car unlocked so Oswald placed his rifle in the back seat and sat in the passenger seat to wait. When Buell came out and climbed into his car, he saw the package and asked Oswald, "What's in the package?"

Oswald, irritated, replied, "Don't you remember? It's curtain rods. I told you yesterday I was going to be getting curtain rods that I could take out to my room and put up curtains."

Buell did not mention them again, but when they arrived at work, he wondered why Oswald retrieved the curtain rods from the back seat and carried them in with him. Oswald hurried ahead, too, and did not walk in with Buell.

Oswald stashed the package and entered the Texas School Book Depository building using the back door of the loading docks. In the next few hours, he took the package to the sixth floor, unwrapped his mail-order Carcano, and reassembled it. After stacking boxes near the far-corner window that overlooked Dealey Plaza, he went back downstairs to go to work, as if it were any other day.

1963, November 22, Love Field

President John Fitzgerald Kennedy's right hand was already sore from all the firm, friendly Texas handshakes, yet he continued to shake as many hands as he could while still moving toward his presidential Lincoln.

Looking out past the crowd, the First Lady noticed several young men who looked rugged enough to be farmers, proudly flying a large Texas flag. Other men were flying a large Rebel flag right beside them, trying to overshadow the Lone Star flag.

Two hundred years later, the Civil War still raged in the hearts of some.

She was not sure why all these friendly people and the Secret Service would allow people to display their hatred so openly, but she attributed it to being in the land of the free. The president's wife decided that it was probably best to simply ignore the idiots, like everyone else.

When Kennedy first saw his presidential Lincoln, he wondered why someone had removed the see-through bubble top. *He* certainly did not request to have it removed, but the warm, friendly welcome of all the people who had shown up to greet him at the airport gave him a false sense of security. JFK and his wife continued to greet and speak to enthusiastic supporters.

After a few minutes of getting everyone situated into the motorcade, they were finally ready to pull out and head for downtown Dallas on their way to the Dallas Trade Mart. An ABC affiliate news crew began filming. Two Secret Service agents jogged alongside the presidential Lincoln. Sensing they were finally underway, Kennedy and the First Lady turned to toss one last wave to the friendly Texas crowd.

Besides the obvious Rebel flag that fluttered in the stiff breeze, the first real indication that they very well could be in serious trouble was when Agent Emory P. Roberts stood up abruptly in the follow-up car behind the president. He shouted an order to the two running agents, who stood down. One of them jumped onto the running board of the follow-up car. Another agent, Henry J. Rybka, was so shocked by the order that his bewilderment could be seen by his body language. As the motorcade rolled by without him, his hands gestured in animated shrugs three separate times, each conveying more disbelief than the last. Few Americans took their job as seriously as Rybka did, so the Secret Service agent simply *could not* believe what was happening.

Kennedy wondered what was going on, but the trust he had in the Secret Service was unquestioning and complete, and a small amount of conversation with Texas Governor Connally, a fellow former Navy man, distracted the Kennedys pleasantly while the entire motorcade drove away. Rybka was left standing there, frustrated, angry, and unable to do the job he took so seriously.

As Vice President Johnson's car rolled by Rybka, no one made eye contact. Every man in that car knew that he was one of the few people in America who would, without question or hesitation, put his body between the president and however many bullets he could stop before the life drained from his own body.

The president's life was out of Rybka's hands as the motorcade wove its way in and out of traffic on the way to Trade Mart via downtown Dallas.

1963, November 22, Dallas

Bonnie Ray Williams, Harold "Hank" Norman, Charles Givens, and three other coworkers were laying a new floor down in the southwest section of the sixth floor of the Texas School Book Depository. The floors in the building were so old and thin that light shone through holes and between the boards down to the fifth floor.

Over the past four weeks, Williams had regularly seen Lee Harvey Oswald filling orders for school books. They had not spoken to each other at all, but Williams could tell that Oswald was discontent and angry, for he had witnessed him kicking boxes in frustration and muttering to himself about politics.

On November 22, 1963, around 11:45 a.m., Williams and the rest of the construction crew broke for lunch a little earlier than normal in anticipation of the presidential motorcade. The young men "raced" the two elevators down to the first floor as they had enjoyed doing over the past few weeks.

As they were stepping out of the elevator, Givens realized he had left his cigarettes in a pocket of his jacket upstairs, so he took the elevator back up to retrieve them. While there, he saw Oswald with a clipboard, walking from the southwest corner of the floor towards the elevators.

Givens asks Oswald, "Boy, are you going downstairs? It's near lunchtime."

Oswald replied curtly, "No, sir. When you get downstairs, close the gate to the elevator and send it back up."

Givens knew that if the gate to the west elevator was left open, the car would not come when someone on another floor called it, so he agreed to the "request" and took the east elevator back down. However, when he got back down to the first floor, he noticed that the gate to the west elevator was closed and the elevator was not on the first floor.

A few seconds later, when Williams finished washing up, he retrieved his lunch sack and, taking the east elevator back up to the sixth floor, he chose a spot in the southeast corner that overlooked Dealey Plaza. He began eating his lunch alone, wondering where his coworkers were. He saw no one else on the sixth floor, nor did he hear movement from the noisy elevators. At approximately 12:05 or 12:10 p.m., he left his lunch sack, now partially full of trash, and a Dr. Pepper bottle at their work site and rode back down on the east elevator to see if he could find his coworkers downstairs.

On the fifth floor, he joined Hank and James "Junior" Jarmen, Jr. at an open window in the southwest corner. Together, they waited for the motorcade without realizing that they were looking out of a window directly below a sniper. Everyone's world was about to change.

Around 12:30 p.m., as they watched President Kennedy turn from North Houston Street to Elm Street, the first shot in Dealey Plaza exploded with a deafening blast. Pigeons fluttered away furiously.

Williams, Norman, and Jarmen were startled, but thought the noise was a motorcycle backfiring. However, the explosion was so loud that they felt the building shake and heard the windows rattle. Dust and debris from the thin ceiling above them fell on the three men.

In a few short seconds, Norman heard the clinking of brass hitting the thin floor above them as the sniper ejected the shell and loaded another round. A second explosion shook the building and windows again. More debris fell upon them.

Another shell clinked onto the floor above them. Jarmen, finally realizing what was happening, exclaimed, "Man, someone is shooting at the president!"

One last explosion trembled the building and windows. More dust fell on them, and one last shell fell to the floor above them.

When the president's Lincoln was out of sight, Williams, Norman, and Jarmen ran down the stairs, encountering a policeman on the first floor who shouted, "No one leave the building!" They informed that officer that they heard the sniper above them, on the sixth floor. They were searched and told to remain there with other coworkers.

From his motorcycle, Dallas police officer M.L. Baker heard the three shots and determined that they originated from above his head in the Texas School Book Depository. He jumped off his bike and entered the building with his service revolver drawn, where he encountered the building superintendent, Roy Sansom Truly. Together, they began a floor-by-floor search. They tried the elevators, but they were held up somewhere above them. Not hearing the elevators operating, they took the stairs.

On the second floor, Baker and Truly encountered Oswald in the lunchroom. Baker asked Truly if Oswald was an employee there, and Truly confirmed that he was, so they moved on. Oswald, seemingly unaffected by the encounter, remained silent. When the two continued up the stairs, Oswald casually bought a bottle of Coca-Cola. At some point, he realized that the plan to kill Kennedy had been executed. Oswald was probably shocked, but managed to slip out of the building, undetected.

Did the sniper who actually pulled the trigger leave with Oswald? Was the assassin dressed as a law enforcement officer so that he could leave the building without being questioned? Or did he use the cover of chaos to exit with his rifle?

Dallas Deputy Sheriff Roger Craig was in Dealey Plaza after the shooting and claimed that at 12:42 p.m., he saw Oswald run down the grassy slope, whistle to an African American in a Nash Rambler, get into the car, and drive away. When Oswald was questioned about this, he became angry and exclaimed that the "station wagon belonged to Mrs. Paine." In his typical, narcissistic attitude, he insisted that they not involve her, as she had nothing to do with the mess he was in. "Station wagon." Not Nash Rambler.

Later, Williams, Norman, Jarmen, and several other coworkers were escorted to a squad car so they could be transported to the police station to officially make their statements. While Williams and a coworker, Danny Arce, were being loaded into the car, a reporter took a photograph.

In that photo, you can still see the dust and debris from the ceiling that had fallen on Williams.

1963, November 22, Fort Worth

In a typical suburban neighborhood of young trees, brick homes, and struggling new lawns, you could stand atop a hill in the neighborhood park and gaze east for a beautiful view. Dark green forests of oak, elm, and pecan trees might be beginning to show hints of auburn winter colors. The teeming forests harbor squirrels, mockingbirds, deer, and lush, slow-rolling streams and rivers on their way to the Gulf of Mexico. In those waterways thrived catfish, bass, and crayfish.

If you could tear your eyes from the beauty of the forests and rivers to turn around to face west, the most striking thing you might notice would be the significant change in the environment. Cactus, scrub oaks, roadrunners, Texas horned lizards—"horny toads" or "horned frogs" to the locals—and dry creek beds with fossil-laden limestone banks. In the evenings, which were usually warm or hot, it was easy to imagine cowboys riding horses off into breathtaking blazing-orange sunsets. The neighborhood was truly developed on the very ground where The West began.

Inside one of these modest homes, a piece of the *Dallas Morning News* lay uncharacteristically discarded in the trash, soaking up the stains from an unfinished bowl of oatmeal and a banana peel. The newspaper was opened to page fourteen, which was a full-page ad placed by the "American Fact-Finding Committee," a local organization affiliated with the John Birch Society. The ad asked a dozen rhetorical questions of President Kennedy, accusing him of being soft on communism—the ultimate insult of the day and equivalent to making serious accusations of treason.

The ad had three prominent features: a sarcastic headline that "welcomed" Kennedy to Dallas, the unnecessary use of a complete full page for the so-called ad, and the fact that the notice was outlined by a thick black border that the paper typically used only around obituaries. A not-so-prominent feature of the page credited Ted Dealey as the paper's publisher. This was only partially noticeable because of the way the paper was folded and creased, as though someone twisted it before they discarded it. The publisher had not only *approved* the full-page ad, he had personally approved *of* the ad, no matter how inappropriate the content was for a well-respected newspaper to print.

Ted Dealey's sponsorship of the advertisement was significant because it was not simply a matter of a publisher approving a political ad for a newspaper. In the past, Dealey was rarely so involved with the paper's day-to-day operations, such as approving or rejecting the content of ads, political or otherwise. In this instance, he had sent away the staff members responsible for content of this nature.

On the very day that the president of the United States was in town, the employees who would have stopped such an inappropriate ad were out of town, "on assignment," also a rare occurrence for this type of staff.

Ted Dealey simply did not possess the same ethics as his father and grandfather, both named George Dealey. Ted's father, George "G.B." Bannerman Dealey, had served as publisher of the *Dallas Morning News* since 1885 and had purchased the majority shares in 1926. G.B. had treated the paper and his employees with respect, but in the 1940s, he reluctantly began giving his son control so that he could retire.

G.B. had accomplished much more in Dallas than simply establishing a newspaper. In the late 1800s, after the brief but nostalgic "cowboy" days prior to 1890, he had helped Big D change from a saloon town existing only because it was on the trail to Fort Worth into something more family friendly.

In the early 1900s, G.B. also led the efforts to clean up the Trinity River and organized a significant overhaul of the west side of Dallas. He never held a public office of any kind, yet he was such a well-respected and involved citizen that Dallas City Council members voted to name an open square on the west side after him—Dealey Plaza.

Ted Dealey, was quite a different personality. Since his father's death in 1946, the way he managed the *Dallas Morning News*, and his life in general, resulted in losing the respect of the citizens who had admired his father. His lifestyle bled into the newspaper so often that he had begun to accrue respect from hate groups. Ironically, it seemed that more and more decent people were learning to hate him daily.

This morning's full-page ad was finding its way into the trash all across the Fort Worth/Dallas Metroplex, a testament to the exasperation felt by the newspaper's circulation.

Was the full-page, obituary-like ad a prediction that Kennedy might die if he came to Dallas? A promise? *Dealey* Plaza.

Coffee grounds were also dumped onto the ad, purposefully smearing the smear campaign against a beloved president. A young housewife and mother, too busy with daily chores to worry about such political nonsense for long, headed for the back door with a laundry basket under one arm and a blue-eyed, blonde-haired, three-year-old boy in tow.

The little boy, wearing his favorite Superman shirt, began to play between the sheets hanging from a clothesline. His mother hung more laundry with little wooden soldiers. He was too young to realize how nice the freshly laundered clothes smelled, but he knew he was supposed to help by staying close and not pulling any of the clean laundry down on top of him (again).

Dangling sheets and towels had become an imaginary fort where his genetic makeup guided his thought processes into pretending he was protecting people from perilous danger. This zeal to protect the unprotected was in his blood, passed on from his ancestors for many generations.

Intensifying his imagination were the eerie sounds of a relatively warm North Texas November breeze droning relentlessly in the background. Occasionally, as was the case today, wind passing through these plains and forests at just the right speed sounded like the members of an all-male choir off in the distance, individually preparing their voices for some ghostly composition.

The breeze picked up and the laundry danced, adding excitement to the little boy's playtime. The neighbor's screen door slammed shut, and somehow he knew playtime was over. The woman next door half ran and half walked up to his mother, sobbing hysterically. The boy grabbed and held a windblown sheet so that he could poke his head around the end of a row of damp laundry. His mother appeared concerned and a bit frightened.

Still sobbing uncontrollably, their neighbor waved her arms around, pounding her fists against nothing as she tried to tell his mother something. Because she was using words he had never heard, it was hard for him to follow. The little boy's big brother came running out of the house and grabbed his mother's leg, looking up at the two women. As witness to the hysteria, he began to cry as well.

The mother put one hand on his brother's head and her other hand over her mouth to stifle the cry that was puckering her face. Seeing his mother weep was too much. The little boy hurried over to the group and tried to latch onto his mother's other leg, but his big brother pushed him away as though there was only so much mommy to go around and "pecking order" had already been established.

Being the younger sibling, the boy was already used to this behavior from his brother and simply accepted the situation. Looking up at his mother with big eyes, he asked, "What's wrong, Mommy?"

Instead of an answer from his mother, however, between frenzied sobs, the neighbor nearly screamed the piercing words that would always remain one of the boy's earliest memories, haunting him for the rest of his life.

"***The president's—***" she gasped twice while her chest and shoulders heaved with her staccato sobs, "***—been SHOT!***" She had thrust her head forward with the last word, as if to punctuate the sentence, and it served to sear the moment into his young mind.

"***The president's—***" gasp, gasp, "***—been SHOT!***"

The chilling, wild hysteria that dominated the woman's eyes would never leave the little boy's memory, either. Like so many other young women of the time, she was smitten by John F. Kennedy and had most likely entertained the common, secret fantasy that someday they would meet and he would fall hopelessly in love with her. The irrationality and dreaded feelings of unrecoverable loss she was experiencing were genuine, nonetheless, and shared by millions, worldwide.

The little boy's three-year-old mind had no real idea what all this meant. Nor was the child able to comprehend the impact the assassination would have on so many different aspects of world events, both in the near future and for many decades to come. Seeing his mother, his neighbor, and his big brother cry assured him that something terrible had occurred, and even though he didn't know why, he began to cry as well.

1963, November 22, Dallas, Oak Cliff

Fifteen minutes after three high-powered shots rang out in Dealey Plaza, Officer J. D. Tippit was gunned down in the Oak Cliff section of Dallas, near the boarding house where Oswald was staying.

The WWII veteran had been on the lookout for anyone matching the description of the man suspected of shooting Kennedy and Connally. The dispatcher had described the shooter as “a slender white male in his early thirties, 5’10” tall, and weighing about 165 pounds.”

Oswald was 5’9” and weighed about 130 pounds.

Tippit pulled up next to someone who roughly matched the description of the taller, heavier suspect. They exchanged a few words through the open vent window, but then the officer exited his vehicle, leaving the car door open, and walked to the front of the car. The suspect pulled a pistol and fired five shots at Tippit. Three shots struck him in the chest, and another hit him in the right temple. One of the shots missed.

An ambulance rushed the officer to Methodist Hospital, but he had died at the scene.

1963, November 22, New Orleans

Both Jack and Bobby Kennedy had worked very hard for years and put monumental efforts and significant resources into bringing Calogero Minacore, a.k.a. Carlos Marcello, and his brother Joe to justice. On this final day of a three-week trial for Calogero's identification falsification charges and both of the brothers' deportation charges, Judge Herbert W. Christenberry seemed to be taking his time preparing the jury for deliberations.

On and on, the judge lectured, being more thorough than he ever had before. As he repeated some instructions for the third time, a man stepped into the courtroom and handed the bailiff a note while whispering something into his ear. The bailiff rushed over to the judge and handed him the note.

Appearing to be quite shocked, the judge turned away from the rest of the courtroom and faced the jury members with purpose. He announced with some animation that President Kennedy had been shot that morning in Dallas and died a few minutes later.

As the courtroom erupted into an uproar, several of the jurors looked out at Marcello and noticed that he was stoic and unemotional, staring at each jury member until he made eye contact with them all. His brother Joe, their attorney, G. Wray Gill, *and* David Ferrie were all unemotional as well, staring at the jury members, glaring at them through cruel, uncaring eyes.

Distraught but obliging, the courtroom slowly became deathly quiet at the rapping of a large wooden gavel. Judge Christenberry continued, informing the jury that the trial would proceed as planned, despite a tragedy that should cause a nation to pause. He announced to the court that Calogero Minacore, a.k.a. Carlos Marcello, a citizen of New Orleans, deserved his final day in court after enduring weeks of court hearings.

Less than two hours later, after a trial that lasted three weeks, the terrified Big Easy jury returned with their verdict, which was, of course, *not guilty*.

1963, November 23, Washington, DC

At 10:01 a.m., FBI Director Hoover called President Johnson and relayed that the suspect held for the Kennedy assassination had been impersonated in phone calls to the Soviet Embassy in Mexico City.

Hoover explained that the CIA operatives and FBI agents had confirmed that the man who identified himself as Lee Oswald and phoned the Soviet Union was not the man his men had questioned in Dallas.

Johnson ordered all the FBI and CIA memos and records pertaining to the impersonation events in Mexico City destroyed or marked as Top Secret.

Most of the records disappeared, but the Soviet Embassy in Mexico City retained copies of the photographs and records of the impersonator's visits.

1963, November 25, Fort Worth

The little blonde-haired boy and his big brother and mother watched the nation's saddest funeral on a black-and-white TV set. He watched another little boy, who appeared to be about his own age, put his hand to his forehead at the urging of his mother. "What's he doing, Mommy?"

A young, sweet but sad voice barely whispered, "He's saluting his father."

"Why?"

His mother didn't answer because tears welled in her eyes and her throat was tight.

The grief was far worse for the former First Lady, though, knowing that, eerily, she and Jack had taught John F. Kennedy Jr. to salute only a few days before, indeed, capturing the lessons on 8mm home movies.

It would be many years before John Jr. understood the honor that salute bestowed upon his father, the entire nation, and millions of others. It was also entirely possible that he would not live long enough to understand fully, but in November of 1963, neither he nor the little blonde-haired boy in Fort Worth could come close to comprehending the loss of a president or father quite yet.

The mothers of the boys understood well enough, though, as did most people all over the world. Many openly cried.

Most of these decent, respectable people weren't even *capable* of understanding the hatred that others felt toward the Kennedy family. Some people fostered an abhorrence so deep and powerful that they rejoiced as the funeral aired across the globe. In still others, though few, the hatred penetrated even deeper.

One such man, perched unsteadily on a bar stool in the French Quarter of New Orleans, watched the funeral, throwing back drink after drink. He barked inappropriate and offensive comments as the other patrons tried to watch the funeral and observe a traditional moment of silence. Some simply left the bar when the drunken man spewed an especially malicious comment as John Jr. saluted his father.

"Humph! Happy birthday, ya little bastard."

1963, November–2005, January 7

One week after Lyndon Baines Johnson was sworn into the presidency, he ordered the creation of the President's Commission on the Assassination of President Kennedy. Most people know that team as the Warren Commission, the nickname derived from the group's chairman, Chief Justice Earl Warren. They were also tasked with investigating the assassination of the alleged assassin, Lee Harvey Oswald, by Jack Ruby two days after Kennedy was shot.

Ironically, that report convinced many people that the United States government was guilty of assassinating its own president, or at least taking part in distracting people from the truth. The findings of the report produced by the Warren Commission were supposed to prove that a single gunman, acting alone, shot JFK and Governor Connally.

Most people understood that the investigation was either a total farce, or the commission members were tragically incompetent.

However, too much misinformation/disinformation in the report was too brilliantly distracting for *all* the members to be incompetent. It was not surprising that many people believed the commission was probably set up to distract people from the truth—an unsuccessful effort, which brought the possibility of incompetency back into question. The truth was difficult-to-impossible to know.

The people assigned to the commission were suspect from day one. *Allen Dulles?!* Someone whom everyone knew hated Kennedy with a passion? Appointed to the commission to investigate the murder of the man he abhorred? The Warren Commission should have been *investigating* Dulles *and* the agency he controlled during the assassination.

To sharpen the point, commission members were chosen because they were "outstanding citizens," yet more than half were *attorneys*. And as most people were aware, attorneys *swore an oath* to withhold their client's information from the courts, and from the public, even if that truth is an admission of guilt. To become an attorney, one must swear an oath to the American Bar Association to lie and/or hide the truth about their client.

Firmly embedding the point, no one on the Warren Commission had any real investigative experience. There were *no investigators* assigned to the Warren Commission.

Why? Incompetence? Or a deliberate path to the obfuscation of the truth?

If experienced investigators had reviewed the thousands of pages, photos, and films gathered by the commission, it is conceivable that the Warren Report might have still been forced to come to the same conclusion. Conceivable, but highly unlikely.

Overwhelming evidence suggested that Oswald *could not* have killed JFK.

The scope on Oswald's Carcano was still in its factory configuration. The rifle lacked the shims required for sighting the scope in, which probably meant that Oswald never sighted it in. Anyone using the scope would have missed any target more than a couple of feet away, and the scope would have blocked any sighting down the barrel. Also, any competent investigator would question why no one even smelled the rifle barrel that day to see if it had been fired.

A fresh palm print that had disturbed dust on one of the boxes in front of the infamous Texas School Book Depository sixth floor window "sniper's nest" was *not* Oswald's. They found the fingerprints and palm prints of several other employees on the boxes, and Oswald's on only two boxes. Someone else moved that box there, yet no one pursued that suspect. Practically no one referred to that print, yet many "investigators" made an exaggerated issue of finding Oswald's print on his rifle. His own prints on his own rifle. That print was on the barrel, under the stock.

The bullet fragments removed from Connally were not tested to determine the type of bullet and therefore the kind of firearm that fired it. There is also the possibility that the fragments *were* tested, but the results were withheld from the investigation.

In 1978, the House Assassination Committee tested the bullet fragments. Their conclusion was that the bullet that struck Connally's wrist *could* have been Mannlicher-Carcano ammunition fired by Oswald's Carcano rifle. Others made irrefutable claims that the chain of custody of the bullet fragments was compromised more than once. The evidence tested in 1978 did not even weigh the same as the evidence from 1963.

Evidence left on the curb of Main Street from the ricocheted bullet that struck James T. Tague in the cheek *was* spectrographically analyzed. The conclusion determined that the bullet that struck the curb, and possibly Tague's cheek, lacked copper, which meant the projectile could have just been a fragment. However, that trace of material from the curb was decidedly *not* from Mannlicher-Carcano ammunition, so that bullet could not have been fired from Oswald's Carcano rifle. Nor could it have come from the spent Mannlicher-Carcano cartridges found in the "sniper's nest."

Most likely, the expended Mannlicher-Carcano cartridges were planted, and some other rifle was fired at the president.

Those few people who still believed that Lee Harvey Oswald shot President Kennedy were possibly thinking, *Okay, so,*

Oswald brought his rifle in to work that day, but then used some other *rifle.* The deciding factor here should be the fact that the paraffin wax test proved Oswald hadn't fired a weapon that day. Not at Kennedy, Connally, or Tippit.

A handful of others claimed that the paraffin test was inaccurate in 1963, but that was simply not true. Those same people were just as likely to say that the test was extremely accurate when the situation suited them. The facts were conclusive. They found the exact type of chemicals one would find on someone working in the environment he was in, and no other chemicals. Specifically, no fired gunpowder residue. None.

Had Oswald fired a rifle that day, he would have had enough gunpowder residue on him to be detectable for days, even after a shower. Even if he had only fired a pistol at Officer Tippit, as he was accused, he still would have had gunpowder residue on his hand and arm. He did not.

Presented with a mere *subset* of these facts, even an incompetent investigator would have determined that Oswald could not have shot Kennedy or Officer Tippit. If it had been a legitimate investigation, even the *least* experienced among them would have begun assembling an alternative list of suspects.

Make no mistake about it, though, they should not have simply turned their suspect loose. Oswald knew something about who else was involved. *He brought his rifle to work* that morning and left it somewhere for someone to use in the assassination of an American president.

From November 1963 to September 1964, *staggering* were the resources consumed by the Warren Commission, very likely to distract the public from a few key facts concerning the assassination of John F. Kennedy. But why? What was the point of that?

What did "they" not want the American people to know? What fact, lie, or conspiracy could be so hurtful or damaging that Americans couldn't handle the truth, no matter what that truth might be? What could possibly hurt more than a beloved president being shot to death?

And who are "they" anyway? Politicians not wanting to be thrown out of office for failing America and the rest of the world? Or were "they" the people who orchestrated the assassination?

If the government came clean and told the truth about the assassination and the cover-up, would anyone believe them?

Few would.

For most, the truth would likely be viewed as another lie.

The Press, as it was commonly called back then, had feared the relatively mild-mannered JFK, but were not at all afraid of the tough and brash "Master of the Senate" and regular tough-guy from Texas. They brazenly hounded the Johnson administration relentlessly over the Warren Commission and the investigation in general.

Reporters pounded away at LBJ like no president had ever experienced before. Yet *no one* pressured him about the second most important question of the twentieth century: Why was a "commission" investigating the assassination rather than the professionals who were responsible for the investigation? Dallas Police Department detectives. Deputies at the Dallas County Sheriff's Office. A Texas Ranger. Special agents at the FBI. The United States Attorney General's Office.

The general public should have been *inundated* with reports about how the U.S. government forced a commission of people with little to no investigative experience to "investigate" the assassination. Not qualified law enforcement agents, but politicians and attorneys.

Eventually, there were court rulings, and several different conclusions were reached by various government entities. *None* of those conclusions accounted for the trajectories of all three bullets fired that day in Dealey Plaza. Nor did any of these investigations bother to list any other possible suspects for the assassination or for the numerous cover-ups after the fact.

For decades, people have wondered if President Lyndon Johnson knew anything about JFK's assassination, either before or after the fact. Was he responsible? Had he been coerced? Did men come to him after the assassination and tell him that if he didn't cooperate with their ideas of what should happen in Vietnam, he'd meet the same fate as Kennedy?

Why else would Johnson immediately reverse JFK's decision to pull out of Southeast Asia? And why would he order JFK's Lincoln rebuilt so soon after the assassination? And get politicians to fill the Warren Commission instead of investigators.

President Gerald Ford served on the Warren Commission ten years before he became president in 1974. Did he help cover up the assassination? Was he promised the White House for his cooperation? Or was President Nixon coerced into giving the presidency to Gerald Ford to reward him for his previous role in the cover-up of the century?

Was Robert F. Kennedy assassinated because he was a Kennedy trying to get back into the White House? Or was his untimely death in retaliation for the assassination of Dr. Martin Luther King Jr.? Whatever the reason, this left only one of Joe and Rose Kennedy's four sons alive.

The Kennedy family was plagued by untimely deaths, including the deaths of their grandchildren, many of whom Rose survived. Out of all the deaths in the family, with the exception of John and Jackie's infant deaths, the January 7, *2005*, death of Rose Maria Kennedy was the first that occurred naturally. At least two Joe and Rose Kennedy children were murdered, and Jack's assassination remains unsolved.

STATE OF TEXAS — CERTIFICATE OF DEATH — STATE FILE NO.

1. PLACE OF DEATH
a. COUNTY: Dallas
b. CITY OR TOWN: Dallas
c. LENGTH OF STAY: 2 Hrs.
d. NAME OF HOSPITAL OR INSTITUTION: Parkland Memorial
e. IS PLACE OF DEATH INSIDE CITY LIMITS? YES XX NO

2. USUAL RESIDENCE
a. STATE: District of Columbia
b. COUNTY
c. CITY OR TOWN: Washington
d. STREET ADDRESS: 600 Pennsylvania Avenue
e. IS RESIDENCE INSIDE CITY LIMITS? YES XX NO
f. IS RESIDENCE ON A FARM? YES NO XX

3. NAME OF DECEASED: John Fitzgerald Kennedy
4. DATE OF DEATH: November 22, 1963
5. SEX: Male
6. COLOR OR RACE: White
7. Married ☒ Never Married ☐ Widowed ☐ Divorced ☐
8. DATE OF BIRTH: May 29, 1917
9. AGE: 46
10. USUAL OCCUPATION: President of the U.S.
KIND OF BUSINESS OR INDUSTRY: United States Govt.
11. BIRTHPLACE: Brookline, Mass.
12. CITIZEN OF WHAT COUNTRY: U. S. A.
13. FATHER'S NAME: Joseph P. Kennedy
14. MOTHER'S MAIDEN NAME: Rose Fitzgerald
15. WAS DECEASED EVER IN U.S. ARMED FORCES? YES — WW II
16. SOCIAL SECURITY NO.
17. INFORMANT: Evelyn Lincoln

18. CAUSE OF DEATH
PART I. DEATH WAS CAUSED BY: IMMEDIATE CAUSE (a) Multiple gunshot wounds of the head & neck. — INTERVAL BETWEEN ONSET AND DEATH: Minutes
DUE TO (b)
DUE TO (c)
PART II. OTHER SIGNIFICANT CONDITIONS CONTRIBUTING TO DEATH BUT NOT RELATED TO THE TERMINAL DISEASE CONDITION GIVEN IN PART I (a)
19. WAS AUTOPSY PERFORMED? YES ☒ NO ☐

20a. ACCIDENT ☐ SUICIDE ☐ HOMICIDE XX
20b. DESCRIBE HOW INJURY OCCURRED: Shot by a high powered rifle
20c. TIME OF INJURY: 12:31 P.M. 11 22 63
20d. INJURY OCCURRED: WHILE AT WORK / NOT WHILE AT WORK
20e. PLACE OF INJURY: 400 Blk Elm St. Dallas, Tex
20f. CITY, TOWN, OR LOCATION: Dallas — COUNTY: Dallas — STATE: Texas

21. Held Inquest November 22, 1963, 1:00 P.M.
22. SIGNATURE: [signature] J.P.
ADDRESS: 305 N. 5th St. - Garland, Texas
DATE SIGNED: 12-6-63

23a. BURIAL, CREMATION, REMOVAL: Removal
23b. DATE: 11-22-63
23c. NAME OF CEMETERY OR CREMATORY: Arlington National Cemetery
23d. LOCATION: Washington, D.C.
24. FUNERAL DIRECTOR'S SIGNATURE: O'Neal Inc. [signature]
25. REGISTRAR'S FILE NO.: 6820
26. DATE REC'D BY LOCAL REGISTRAR: Dec. 11, 1963
27. REGISTRAR'S SIGNATURE: J W Bass BY Maurine Lamm, Acting Registrar

DALLAS, TEXAS Nov. 25 19 64
I HEREBY CERTIFY THAT THIS IS A TRUE COPY OF DEATH CERTIFICATE OF ONE John Fitzgerald Kennedy AS IS RECORDED IN THIS OFFICE IN THE CITY OF DALLAS, COUNTY OF DALLAS, STATE OF TEXAS.

J. W. Bass
BY Maurine Lamm
ACTING CITY REGISTRAR OF VITAL STATISTICS
DALLAS, TEX.

Common Misconceptions Clarified

• "The magic bullet." The *magic* bullet. Nothing says "poor investigative skills" more than claiming that the bullet that also struck Connally would have had to have been magic. Conspiracy theorists in the multiple-shooter camp have jetted out countless tangents because they didn't believe one bullet could cause four wounds. *Seven* wounds, if you count entry and exit wounds separately.

While much of the Warren Commission was tragically incorrect, what it concluded about the origin of the shots was accurate. No matter how much a handful of people wanted there to be multiple shooters in multiple locations, there were not. All three shots originated from that sixth floor window, and one bullet caused four of their wounds. Some people didn't understand the logistics of the assassination, so they discredited the truth and circulated misinformation/disinformation.

Some even called the facts about the neck shot "the single bullet theory." Calling it a theory, or using the phrase "the magic bullet," tended to push people with conspiracy tendencies into the realms of fiction. This was *evidence*, not theory. Other investigations use the correct terminology. The assassination of a president should, too.

Determining the trajectory of that second shot is easy once you examine the evidence. The facts become conclusive when the position of Governor Connally is considered. The "rumble seats" where he and Mrs. Connally sat were positioned both lower than the back seat and a small distance away from the car doors to allow for passengers to step back to the rear seat. Because Connally was seated slightly inboard from JFK, the governor leaned over to his left as he turned around to his right to face Kennedy after he heard the first shot.

Knowing all this, it is easy to follow the trajectory of that not-so-magical bullet.

When the second gunshot in Dealey Plaza struck Kennedy's neck, it caused his arms to retract into what's known as Thorburn's Position. This only occurs when there is damage to the C6 or C7 vertebra. The bullet passed through his neck at a downward angle of about eighteen to nineteen degrees, nicking the upper left side of the knot in his tie.

The projectile continued on and also passed through Connally's torso, who we now know had leaned over to his left as he turned around to his right. The bullet entered his upper back, near the right shoulder, and exited just below the right nipple, then through his right wrist because his arm was bent at the elbow. The bullet finally lodged itself into the governor's thigh.

Those wounds line up perfectly for a shot originating from the infamous sixth floor window of the Texas School Book Depository, which has since been renamed the Dallas County Administration Building.

No magic was involved. There is no need for childlike theories, misinformation, or distraction tactics. The evidence for one shooter is clear now, so there is no longer a reason to suggest alternate theories that suggest multiple shooters.

• The most commonly held misbelief is the notion that the "back and to the left" motion of Kennedy's head meant that a shot had to have originated from in front of Kennedy. The misinformation/disinformation surrounding the horrific shot to the head was burned into the collective minds of the public when Life magazine published the frames of the film as stills. However, because of their agreement with Zapruder, Life magazine omitted frame 313 from its publication.

Jim Garrison, the district attorney of Orleans Parish in Louisiana, successfully subpoenaed the Zapruder film, which was still owned by Life magazine at the time. Garrison and his team watched the film many times but probably did not study it thoroughly, or have anyone qualified analyze it. Did Garrison and his legal team simply overlook the glaring omission of frame 313, or ignore it? (More on this, later.)

Whatever the case, anyone watching the Zapruder film can easily see Kennedy's head move back, and to his left. However, you must slip into analyst mode to see the full motion. Kennedy's head is knocked forward first.

It's true.

Blood, bone, and brain matter were ejected and sprayed as his head moved forward rapidly. Then, moving significantly slower, and with no additional blood spray, JFK's chin bounced off his chest and his hands, which were still near his neck from the Thorburn's Position reaction to the wound from the previous shot. "Back, and to the left" was only two-thirds of Kennedy's reaction to being shot. The full observed motion is: forward, rapidly, then a slower movement back, and to his left.

Why would anyone who wants to know the truth examine two-thirds of the known evidence? Especially when the third being ignored was the most important piece of evidence. And in the case of the assassination of JFK, it was the moment that took Kennedy's life. Frame 313 was the most important piece of evidence.

Three movements. Forward fast, then considerably slower, back, and to his left.

Claiming that a bullet was fired from in front of Kennedy, and ignoring the fact that the shot had to have come from behind and to his right, was always a case of spreading misinformation or disinformation.

Mis/dis.

Once some people believed and possibly defended mis/dis, it was very difficult to get them to consider facts contradicting their beliefs. Getting them to change their mind was often an impossible task. It was as though they believed they had something invested in the mis/dis. They didn't. Once the truth is known to a researcher, amateur or professional, they simply *must* commit to the facts, even if those facts contradict what they previously considered to be true.

Forward rapidly, because a bullet knocked Kennedy's head forward. Then back, much slower than the forward motion, as his head merely bounced off his chest and/or hands, rather than getting struck by a projectile. Again, forward rapidly, then back and to the left because his head bounced, not because it was struck by another bullet.

• While we are on the subject of the Zapruder film, let's address the fact that many people believed that the original film and all the copies had been modified. Admittedly, modified versions of the Zapruder film *are* available, but original, unmodified copies are just as easily found. Unfortunately, people have used modified versions to support their notion of what happened. When the Zapruder film showed what they believed, they pointed and said, "There! See?" But when parts of the film contradicted their beliefs, they exclaimed, "The film's been altered!"

Downloading all the copies of the Zapruder film from credible sources and comparing them will ease most people's minds. Purposefully searching for modified versions will help people understand as well. Most people will be able to determine that the digitized frames have been modified. Even those with little-to-no experience in detecting modified images will likely be able to tell which versions are original and which have modifications.

• One of the possible sources of the rumors suggesting that the original Zapruder film had been modified originated from the deal reached between Abraham Zapruder and Life magazine. After Zapruder accepted $150,000 from Life magazine for his film (equivalent to well over a million dollars in the economy of the 2020s) he felt guilty after having a nightmare. He asked Life to prevent people from seeing "the President's head explode" by removing frame 313. When Life magazine made the images of the film public, they honored Zapruder's wish and did not show frame 313.

The original film, in its entirety, including frame 313 and all the pre-Dealey Plaza footage of grandchildren and coworkers, is easily available on several trustworthy websites. Zapruder died in 1970, but in 1975, Life magazine sold the film back to the Zapruder family for one dollar, then in 1999, the family donated the copyright of the entire film to the Sixth Floor Museum.

Anyone who has any interest in the assassination of John F. Kennedy should probably watch the original, unmodified Zapruder film and decide for themselves where the head shot likely originated.

• The most commonly misguided JFK *venture* was, and still is, trying to prove whether or not there was a conspiracy. Were multiple people involved, or was it an act of a lone gunman? A mere *subset* of the evidence makes this endeavor a complete waste of time. Even though there was only one shooter (and maybe a spotter) multiple people *had* to be involved.

It's obvious there was a conspiracy. Let's all move on.

When other murders are investigated, determining whether multiple people were involved is always a part of that, but no one mentions "conspiracy" if multiple people are involved. It's still just a murder. Maybe we could treat JFK's murder like any other investigation.

• Another common misbelief, or lack of understanding, is *when* all three shots were fired. Was the shot that struck Kennedy's neck and wounded Connally the first bullet fired, or the second? Or was the head shot the second bullet fired? Or was that bullet the last one fired?

Witnesses reported hearing a varying number of shots. Most claimed to hear either three or four shots, but not everyone. Contributing to the chaos were the echoes caused by the structures in and around Dealey Plaza. Those echoes made it difficult to determine how many shots were fired and from which direction they came.

Taking the time to read the police reports made that day can be enlightening. There are places in the statements where it is obvious the interviewer asked leading questions, or asked them to affirm things that, in hindsight, might have been incorrect assumptions.

In one police report, thirty-two-year-old Jean Hill testified that she and her friend, Mary Moorman, heard two shots fired as the president's car rounded the corner onto Elm. She claimed JFK grabbed his chest and fell onto Jackie's lap, and then three or four more shots were fired before the motorcade sped away. She also claimed to see a man wearing plain clothes shooting back.

Standing next to Jean Hill was her friend, Mary Moorman, who claimed to have heard three or four shots, but her police report did not mention a man in plain clothes returning fire.

Fifty-seven-year-old S.M. Holland said he only heard two shots fired, but also testified that if he remembered anything else, he'd be sure to "come back and tell Bill."

Ronald Fischer swore in another police report that he saw a man hiding behind boxes in a window on the *fifth* floor of the Texas School Book Depository. He went on to say that he heard four shots coming "from that building there." Presumably, he was pointing at a building, but which building? The report did not specify, which seemed to serve as a testament to the quality of the fact-finding performed by most law enforcement officers that day.

Gayle Newman and her family were nearby and claimed to hear three shots fired, possibly four. Gayle's husband, William, testified to hearing only two gunshots, but they both claimed they saw Kennedy stand up and sit back down after one of the shots.

J.C. Price swore he heard a "volley" of five shots and then, up to five minutes later, one more.

Charles Hester heard two shots come from in or around the Texas School Book Depository, and then there was "utter confusion and chaos" as police ran toward the railroad tracks. He said he finally found someone from the Dallas Sheriff's Office and asked him to go and check out the School Book building.

Eyewitness and earwitness accounts varied wildly. Some of the reports filed were so radically wrong that they *had* to have been made falsely by crackpots trying to feel important. However, those who take the time to read every report about the assassination will find that *most of the statements roughly match what is seen in the Zapruder film*. But it's hard to ignore how inaccurate many of the reports were.

To this day, murky waters are still being darkened by the FBI's scale model of Dealey Plaza in the Sixth Floor Museum. The model has incorrect bullet trajectories displayed with string. The first shot indicated by the model is closer to the trajectory of the second bullet, and the first shot is not included at all.

Everyone who visits the Sixth Floor Museum and views the display stands a good chance of being confused by the incorrect model. The Sixth Floor Museum knowingly and willingly spreads misinformation/disinformation under the guise of "*you* decide." Sad.

Hopefully, thoughts will be made clearer by a review of the shots.

The first shot missed its target entirely. It's possible that the projectile deflected off the arm of the traffic light and landed in the street behind JFK's vehicle. A newer explanation has been put forth by Paul Landis, the Secret Service agent who was riding on the follow-up car with Clint Hill. Landis claims that, after they took Kennedy into the hospital, he found a near-pristine bullet (Sound familiar?) on, or in, the back seat behind where the president had been sitting.

He claims he picked up the bullet and put it in his pocket to keep souvenir hunters from taking it. Pretty much everyone would know to hand that over to the police, or to guard it until an officer could collect that evidence, but that's not what Secret Service Agent Paul Landis did. Instead of handing it over to the police, who were present in droves, he took the bullet into the hospital and secretly placed it on Kennedy's gurney. Not Connally's gurney, where it was later found, but on Kennedy's.

Having no explanation for this bullet found on a gurney created wild rides for many conspiracy theorists. Landis remained silent and resigned from the Secret Service.

Was the bullet the result of a misfire? Or did it land in the rear seat cushion, which slowed the projectile enough for it to still be pristine, and came to rest sticking out of the seat enough for Landis to find? Or did the Secret Service agent plant false evidence?

The bullet found on Connally's gurney was a 6.5-millimeter, copper-jacketed bullet that could have come from a Carcano rifle. Was it the same projectile that Landis claimed he found?

Does any of that matter? The first shot missed.

Most people thought what they heard was a firecracker or a backfire. Many witnesses thought subsequent shots were also fireworks, including Kennedy's driver. Governor Connally wasn't fooled. He knew it was a gunshot and turned to his right to look at Kennedy.

The second shot was relatively easy for the sniper to take because the driver of JFK's Lincoln did not speed away, and may have even slowed down. That second bullet was the one that passed through Kennedy's neck and caused his elbows to contort into Thorburn's Position, with his hands retracted to his neck. The bullet continued through the back of Connally's seat. The governor was still turned around looking at Kennedy when the bullet passed through his torso and his wrist, then became lodged in his thigh.

With the presidential Lincoln still rolling along at a leisurely pace, the sniper had ample time to re-aim and fire the kill shot. This bullet passed through the upper right side of our president's head, breaking out several sections of skull and causing blood and brain matter to spray into the stiff autumn breeze. The projectile continued through the windshield, toward the triple underpass, and either ricocheted off the curb to graze James Tague's right cheek, or caused a piece of concrete from the curb to strike Tague.

One of the dislodged pieces of Kennedy's skull came down and landed on the car's trunk. Jackie witnessed this and, in a state of shock, climbed onto the back of the car to retrieve the skull fragment as Secret Service Agent Clint Hill ran from the following car. He jumped onto the bumper platform and asked her to return to her seat. Jackie held that piece of skull all the way to the hospital where, still in shock, no doubt, she handed it to a surgeon.

• One last misbelief worth mentioning is, *if* there was a conspiracy then there *had* to have been multiple shooters. That is simply not true. There was definitely a conspiracy, which only means that more than one person was involved, but there was still only one shooter. Oswald obviously knew there was a plot to assassinate JFK, but it was not possible for him to have fired the Carcano rifle he brought to work that day, or any other firearm.

Oswald very likely stacked the boxes in front of the window when he stashed his rifle on the sixth floor. His fingerprints and palm prints were found on the boxes, but were not found on the three spent shells left after the assassination, or the bullet still in the chamber. One fresh palm print was found that was not Oswald's and did not match any other employees who worked on the sixth floor, all of whom were fingerprinted. It should be noted that not *all* employees were fingerprinted. Just the ones who normally accessed the sixth floor.

Both elevators had been taken to the fifth floor by the crew replacing the flooring, where they watched the motorcade and witnessed the assassination. They took the stairs down, so the elevators remained there. Several other people were either in the stairwell or could see the stairs, and Oswald did not use them. Officer Baker and the building superintendent, Truly, found Oswald in the lunchroom on the second story moments after the last shot was fired.

Someone besides Oswald was there, with a second rifle that was more powerful than a cheap Carcano, and with a scope that was sighted in.

Consider the accomplices. Oswald was obviously involved, if only because they intended to frame him, and then there was the sniper, who, again, could not have been Oswald. The person or people involved in dismissing the Secret Service agents from the presidential Lincoln, and JFK's driver slowing down instead of speeding away. That's at least four, so far.

There was also the "other" Oswald who used the real Oswald's identity in Mexico City. Was that imposter the man who shot

Officer Tippit, dressed similarly to Oswald that day to deceive witnesses so they would pick him out of the lineup? Or did someone coach or coerce those witnesses? Whoever shot Officer Tippit might also have been involved in the plot at Dealey Plaza. That raises the possible number of accomplices by three more, bringing the possible total to six or more people.

At least two other people were involved in Oswald's assassination attempt of Edwin A. Walker. They, too, could have been involved in the assassination of Kennedy. Already having a relationship established, they could have been the ones to convince Oswald to bring his rifle to work. Now up to nine people.

Jack Ruby could have easily been a part of the plan, too, by taking out "the patsy" before he made a deal or broke down and revealed names. The smirk on Oswald's face seen in many of the photos taken while he was in police custody is indicative of someone trying to keep a secret. That smirk may have been what got him killed. Ruby brings the possible total up to ten people.

Lastly, Secret Service Agent Paul Landis claimed he found a near-pristine bullet in JFK's Lincoln and placed it on the president's gurney. That bullet was later found on Governor Connally's gurney and obviously did not pass through human flesh. Nor did it cause seven wounds. This act may have been an attempt to implicate Oswald, but the fact that the bullet had obviously been fired before it was found made many people assume it was either a message, or planted evidence. Was this an eleventh person?

Did any of those eleven people plan the assassination? Which one of them organized it? Or was an additional planner involved? Someone like Carlos Marcello. Up to a dozen people.

In summary, Oswald was involved. It is possible that one person did all the planning and convinced Oswald to abandon his Carcano on the sixth floor. That person could have also been the sniper *and* the one using Oswald's identity. It's also possible that removing the Secret Service agents from JFK's vehicle and JFK's driver slowing down were simply individual acts of incompetence. The timing of Officer Tippit's murder could have been a coincidence, and Jack Ruby might have been the one who was the lone nut.

So! That's somewhere between a minimum of two (Oswald and the sniper) and at least a dozen people needed to pull off the assassination. Furthermore, many more people were needed after the fact to distract people from the truth so thoroughly.

Okay, So, Who Did It?

Thousands of people were *enraged* by many of John F. Kennedy's decisions and policies, and by his personal abuse of the presidency. Who among them was angry enough to murder him? He also angered so many powerful people that there were *multiple credible plots* to assassinate him. This makes it even more problematic to determine who actually succeeded.

• Lee Harvey Oswald brought his rifle to work the morning JFK was assassinated, knowing that the presidential motorcade would be driving by his place of employment. He was involved in, or at least informed of, at least one of the plots. He knew something sinister was planned.

When Oswald was arrested, he was searched. Twice. Once by Paul Bentley and again by Charles Truman Walker. At the police station, an interrogation began with Oswald handcuffed and denied legal representation. Detectives searched him again two hours later to prepare him for the Helen Markham lineup. Elmer Boyd found several live rounds of ammo in Oswald's left front pants pocket. Richard Sims found a bus ticket in his shirt pocket.

Rarely are prisoners frisked for a lineup. Especially when they were already frisked when they were arrested and had been in police custody for over two hours, under interrogation the entire time.

There are only two likely explanations. Either the Dallas Police Department had acted with incompetence, yet again, or that evidence was planted on Oswald. And yes, both of those scenarios are possible.

As the Warren Commission reviewed Oswald's financial records, they realized (or were forced to make it publicly known) that an additional person had been using Oswald's identity, and that one of them had been paid a salary by the federal government. They immediately sealed his tax records and the tax records of his mother. They are still sealed. Was Oswald's mother paid to remain silent?

Oswald's financial data after he returned from the USSR is available in the Warren Commission report, yet the tax records remain sealed. There is an obvious disconnect when you add the couple's expenses together, and then compare that to their income. Even before considering any frivolous spending, the Oswalds spent more than what was reported in their income.

That is why his tax records remain sealed.

Even though Oswald defected to the USSR and then returned to U.S. citizenry during the height of the Cold War, he blamed Connally for his Undesirable Discharge status after an early release from the U.S. Marines. The "early release" was based on the grounds of hardship but was closer to an act of desertion.

When the presidential motorcade rolled by and shots were fired, witnesses saw Oswald only moments later in the second-floor lunchroom of the Texas School Book Depository building. The elevators were still on the fifth floor, and none of the people who were in the stairwells saw him.

Most of Oswald's coworkers were outside for the motorcade, or at windows overlooking Dealey Plaza, but he was in the lunchroom. Officer Baker and Roy Truly said Oswald was emotionless at a time when nearly everyone in the building heard the gunshots, and a policeman was pointing a gun at his gut.

As Oswald realized that the president had been shot, *surely*, he wondered why the plan to kill Kennedy required his cheap rifle but did not require the sharpshooter skills of the owner of that firearm.

The testimony of the break room witnesses and the lack of gunpowder residue on Oswald is enough to eliminate Oswald as a suspect. If you also consider that his unsighted Carcano rifle couldn't have been used to fire those shots, it becomes irresponsible, or even suspicious, to continue treating Oswald as anything but a red herring accomplice.

Logic nags at even the most amateur of investigators to identify other suspects.

When Oswald was apprehended at the Texas Theatre on W. Jefferson Boulevard, it was under questionable circumstances. Dallas police officers arrived in force to arrest him, and when officers approached Oswald and attempted to take him into custody, he pulled out a .38 revolver, or Officer McDonald tossed it to him, as Oswald claimed. He either did not get off a shot or he chose not to shoot, but a brief scuffle ensued.

Maybe Oswald did not try to shoot his way out of being framed because he knew he would pass a paraffin test, which he did. The test revealed that he had not fired a shot that day. He *did* test positive for the nitrates found in the ink used on the boxes he handled all day, so detectives falsely claimed that negative test results were not always accurate and continued to treat him as a murder suspect, and *still* did not look for other suspects.

Italian Carcano rifles were purposefully designed and manufactured "loosely" to help reduce production costs. When fired, they emit *clouds* of nitrates. Had Oswald fired that weapon, he would have tested positive for gunpowder residue for days. No one even swabbed the barrel of the rifle to see if it had been fired that day, to verify that it was indeed the assassin's weapon. No one even smelled the barrel. Not the Dallas police, not a Dallas County sheriff or deputy, not the FBI, not the Secret Service. No one.

In 1969, Dallas Police Chief Jesse Edward Curry uttered a guilt-altering confession that surprisingly few people have quoted. With shame on his face, Curry said, "We don't have any proof that Oswald fired the rifle, and never did. Nobody's yet been able to put him in that building with a gun in his hand. Why Oswald was nevertheless blamed for the crime seems difficult to explain – but it is what happened."

Some witnesses to the Officer Tippit shooting seemed coerced, or maybe they just wanted their fifteen minutes of fame. However, Domingo Benavides was the closest witness to Tippit's murder. He was parked fifteen to twenty feet diagonally across from Tippit's patrol car, *yet he was not used in a lineup*.

Later, in an interview for the Warren Commission, Benavides said that the pictures of Oswald he had seen on TV and in the newspaper for weeks only resembled the man he had seen shoot Tippit. No wonder the Dallas Police Department didn't want him mucking up their investigation/frame-up of the man they assumed was the killer. Right or wrong, they had the man they were going to prosecute. Or assassinate.

Other people who had claimed to witness Tippit's shooter did not actually see anyone fire a shot. What they witnessed was a man fleeing the scene. Some of the witnesses described the man who fled as having light hair. Others said dark hair. The same inconsistency was used to describe the shooter's clothes. Was that because they didn't really see much, but *did* see photos of Oswald on a black-and-white TV screen?

• Were Dallas police officers behind the assassination and in need of (in Oswald's words) "a patsy?" Or did someone of higher authority lie to them and assure them that Oswald was the assassin and there was no need to pursue other possible suspects? Why were Dallas police so complicit and careless with the investigation? No one recorded the interviews or even took notes until later in the day. Could they *really* have been that incompetent? Or did enough of them hate Kennedy so vehemently that they assassinated our president and tried to frame Oswald as a lone gunman?

• Calogero Minacore, a.k.a. Carlos Marcello, was certainly angry enough to kill JFK, and possibly had orders from Jimmy Hoffa to do so. (This may be the very reason why Hoffa later disappeared without a trace.) But Marcello didn't need another reason to kill his worst enemy. He could have easily arranged to have his people pull off the assassination and frame Oswald. For that matter, this is something *any* of the New Orleans, Chicago, New York, or Miami Beach gangsters could have done.

If Marcello or any other gangster had "ordered the hit," either for himself or for Hoffa, or even the Secret Service, the shooter is most likely lost to history. *No one will ever know who actually pulled the trigger.*

The Family probably would have gotten someone they trusted, who was expendable, to hire a shooter. Immediately after the job was done, that trustworthy gangster would have killed the assassin before he had the chance to talk. Then, that expendable, trustworthy gangster would have also been killed, taking any knowledge of the assassin with him.

• At first, Lyndon B. Johnson insisted that the Dallas Police Department remain in charge of "the local shooting." Were they easier to control? Did he have local, fellow Texans completely loyal to him?

Why were the FBI and CIA memos about the Oswald impersonator in the Mexico City Soviet Embassy ordered destroyed or hidden away by making them Top Secret? Did LBJ think he was protecting U.S. citizens by covering up the information? Or did he simply know that the Soviets were not involved and wanted to avoid the obvious conflicts the information would have sparked?

It was no secret that LBJ and JFK could not stand each other. When Johnson, the "Master of the Senate," lost the primary to Kennedy, his anger and hatred were apparent to everyone in private. In public, his declaration of "LBJ now stands for Let's Back Jack!" was simply a means of getting elected to the vice-presidency, which is one death away from the Oval Office.

If the detail-oriented Johnson had arranged to have Kennedy assassinated, would there have been so many discrepancies in evidence and testimonies? Or would Johnson's plan have been more organized?

• Despite being a family friend of the Kennedys, Chief Justice Earl Warren allowed the CIA, the FBI, and the Secret Service to be responsible for investigating their own agents. He also suppressed some of the facts and evidence in the investigation because he thought they were inappropriate or inconvenient for the Kennedy family. He also ensured that no one on his committee had any real investigative experience.

Pause for a moment, please, and consider that. *No one on the investigative commission had any investigative experience.*

On purpose? Or was it sheer incompetence?

Does the true task of the President's Commission on the Assassination of President John F. Kennedy become obvious? Was it to investigate the assassination? Or was it to make sure that Oswald was blamed for the assassination? Did they hide the truth? How much truth did they hide? Did they help a group of people get away with assassinating a president?

Should every decision-making member of the Warren Commission, along with LBJ, be murder suspects? Or should they have at least been charged with aiding and abetting after the fact?

Because of the Warren Commission, no one was watching the watchers.

• Allen Dulles, the first civilian director of Central Intelligence and the CIA's longest-serving director to date, was also a staunch Republican and *hated* JFK. He could have suppressed or even fabricated incriminating facts for any number of people during the "investigation." Covering his own tracks would have, or must have, been easy.

• Richard M. Nixon really was the crook he claimed not to be, despite making some good decisions and policies while in the White House. He openly declared his hatred for Kennedy *and* his intent to get even with him for making him feel like a fool during the first nationally televised debate.

Nixon openly threatened JFK, again, when he realized the extent of voter fraud used to defeat him in his first bid for the White House. "Tricky Dick" was known for making serious threats, and did so often. He followed through with most of his threats, too, which invariably resulted in damaged or ruined careers, although he was never associated with any *known* deaths.

Still, including Nixon as a suspect in the JFK assassination is not far-fetched. He *did* depart the Fort Worth/Dallas area via Love Field a few minutes before Kennedy landed there on November 22, 1963.

• Castro could have ordered Cuban military personnel to kill Kennedy, or any one of a few thousand angry Cubans could have done so as well, many of whom were already on American soil.

• However unlikely it may seem, Adlai Stevenson was angry enough to have Kennedy taken out, too. He felt that the Kennedys had permanently tarnished the reputation he had so carefully crafted over *decades*. An entire life's work of building the trust of the American people was wiped away because he repeated a few words from someone he considered to be a spoiled brat and too young to be president.

Stevenson had ample resources and was quite an influential man. He could have found a way to take out the highly visible president without raising a single suspicious eyebrow in his direction.

• The senior Secret Service agent at Love Field on November 22, 1963, Emory P. Roberts, ordered the agents that were assigned to Kennedy's presidential vehicle to stand down and abandon their post. If you watch the newsreel of the motorcade leaving Love Field, you can clearly see the frustrated body language of the agents assigned to protect JFK.

The *vice* president's Secret Service agents were *not* ordered to stand down. They stayed with LBJ.

Roberts had also ordered or approved the top of JFK's car to be removed. These decisions were made without JFK's approval or knowledge, and they were made *knowing* there were *multiple* credible threats against the president.

When shots were fired, a Secret Service agent jumped on top of LBJ, the *vice* president. While pushing the VP down to the floorboard and covering his body, he yelled at Lady Bird and Senator Yarborough to get down.

No Secret Service agents were present to jump onto JFK, or drag him to the protection of the floorboard. Or warn Jackie, Governor Connally, and Mrs. Connally.

Adding to the fiasco, the driver of the president's car barely reacted at all, and did not speed up until well after JFK's head was a broken, bloody mess. Clint Hill, the agent assigned to the First Lady (not the president) had time to jump off the following car, *run* to the president's car, and climb onto the back before the Secret Service agent who was driving finally sped up to evacuate the area.

A sniper had plenty of time to fire three rounds at the exposed president. The sniper shouldn't have been able to see JFK long enough to take the *second* shot, but he was able to take aim and fire *three* times.

They left the president of the United States of America completely exposed while a sniper casually fired three rounds. It was the First Lady herself who finally partially covered the president's body with her own, after she climbed onto the trunk to retrieve a skull fragment. It took her a moment to partially recover from shock, but it was Jackie Kennedy who placed her body over our president, not the Secret Service. But of course, it was too late.

• Or did Jackie shield her husband's dead body because she knew no more shots would be fired? Had she become angry enough, or sufficiently humiliated, to arrange the assassination? Every year, enough people are murdered by their spouses for law enforcement agencies to create policies that require them to investigate the surviving spouses of murder victims. Even international reporters knew how angry and humiliated Jackie had been. She probably should have been a suspect.

• The Soviets and the KGB are obvious suspects. This is a no-brainer, but at the time, treating them as suspects might have caused them to retaliate. United States retribution for the retaliation of foreign governments could easily have led to war, which might have led to everyone's worst nightmare of a nuclear exchange. If a foreign government were responsible for the assassination, that could be why LBJ and the Warren Commission put all the blame onto someone else's "patsy."

• Many a Turk also wished ill will upon our fine president in retaliation for striking the nuclear arms deal with the USSR. Removing the American nukes from their country left them wide open and vulnerable to expanding communist societies. Fear and hatred are powerful motivators for revenge.

• Madame "Dragon Lady" Nhu certainly wanted JFK to pay for the deaths of her husband and brother-in-law. She could have sold her shoe collection to fund the assassins. Countless other Southeast Asians also wanted Kennedy dead.

• A union vigilante, a ruthless businessman fuming over lost revenue, a Black Panther, a white supremacist, an East German agent, a rogue FBI, CIA, or Secret Service agent ticked off at JFK's abuse of the services their particular branch provided (such as womanizing or threatening people to achieve some personal goal). A reporter sick of having the truth trampled upon and covered up, a feminist fighting for the rights of her gender, *any*one, in *any* country, livid over the Partial Test Ban Treaty for reasons that might be either pro-treaty or passionately anti-treaty, Ted Dealey, and *maybe* even Aristotle Onassis.

Again, JFK angered so many people that there were *multiple* credible plots to assassinate him. Looking for suspects could go as far back as a resentful crew member of the PT-109. Again, as unlikely as that seems, it's possible. Kennedy rubbed *many* people the wrong way, even though it was rarely intentional.

Several people have confessed to assassinating John F. Kennedy. None could be verified or corroborated. Most of these confessions made claims that included "facts" that could not have been true. Even E. Howard Hunt's first deathbed confession made too many claims contradicting the obvious. He could not be considered a credible suspect.

Sadly, there are many more, less obvious people who should have been seen as suspects. Even though the list of suspects in this book is long, it is nowhere near complete. Still, why were none of the *obvious* suspects ever investigated?

Is it too late?

JFK FYI

www.Jfk.fyi